Dr Michael Valenzuela has been researching dementia and brain ageing since 1999. He won the prestigious Australian Museum Eureka Prize for Medical Research in 2006 for his work linking mental activity with reduced dementia risk.

Dr Valenzuela first worked in psychology in the area of stroke and Vascular Dementia. He then completed medical studies at the University of Sydney and a PhD at the University of New South Wales. He worked as a doctor at the Prince of Wales Hospital in Sydney and returned to research at the School of Psychiatry, University of New South Wales, in 2006. He is now a Senior Research Fellow at the School and leads the Regenerative Neuroscience Group.

Dr Valenzuela has contributed to numerous scientific research publications in the area of brain ageing and dementia. His research has been covered by reports in *The Sydney Morning Herald*, *The Australian*, *Time* magazine, *Business Review Weekly*, the ABC television program *Catalyst* and numerous radio interviews.

Michael likes to practise what he preaches by engaging in a diverse range of leisure activities. He is a keen salsa dancer, trains in martial arts, loves to travel and sail, and is currently trying his hand at gardening.

GW00640655

MAINTAIN YOUR BRAIN

MAINTAIN YOUR BRAIN

What you can do
to improve your brain's
health and avoid dementia

Dr Michael J Valenzuela

Winner of the Eureka Prize for Medical Research

ABC
Books

The ABC 'Wave' device is a trademark of the
Australian Broadcasting Corporation and is used
under licence by HarperCollins*Publishers* Australia.

First published as *It's Never too Late to Change Your Mind* in 2009
by ABC Books for the Australian Broadcasting Corporation.
This updated and retitled edition published 2011
by HarperCollins*Publishers* Australia Pty Limited
ABN 36 009 913 517
harpercollins.com.au

HarperCollins*Publishers*
Level 13, 201 Elizabeth Street, Sydney NSW 2000, Australia
31 View Road, Glenfield, Auckland 0627, New Zealand
A 53, Sector 57, Noida, UP, India
77–85 Fulham Palace Road, London W6 8JB, United Kingdom
2 Bloor Street East, 20th floor, Toronto, Ontario M4W 1A8, Canada
10 East 53rd Street, New York NY 10022, USA

ISBN 978 0 7333 3022 3

Cover design by Darren Holt, HarperCollins Design Studio
Cover image by shutterstock.com
Typeset in Minion 12/21pt
Printed and bound in Australia by Griffin Press
70gsm Classic used by HarperCollins*Publishers* is a natural, recyclable product made from wood
grown in sustainable forests. The manufacturing processes conform to the environmental
regulations in the country of origin, Finland.

5 4 3   12 13 14

This book is dedicated to those fine older Australians who, in my formative years as a medical researcher, welcomed me into their homes and allowed me to probe, poke, stretch and measure their brains without so much as a whimper, and invariably with the offer of a hot cup of tea afterwards.

Contents

Introduction

Dementia can be a frightening illness, initially for the individual, and then for the family. This is because dementia takes away our memories, and then progresses to rob us of our personal style, independence and, finally, bodily control. We fear that a lifetime of achievements, acquired knowledge and experiences could be replaced one day by a state of infant-like dependency. Instead of enjoying our twilight years in a dignified manner among family and friends, we may find ourselves in an anonymous and incomprehensible world, with strangers staring at us, feeding and washing us, telling us what to do, even wiping our backsides.

What can we do to protect ourselves against dementia? This book has been written to address that very question, which is often asked by attendees at my public lectures. There appears to be some level of dissatisfaction among the general public with the information that was available on the World Wide Web and in the media; when it comes to dementia, people want information they can trust. I hope that by clearly outlining what we know (and don't know) about the causes of dementia, and then what we can do to protect ourselves against it, some of the anxiety people feel will be replaced by a greater sense of self-control.

The good news is that the main forms of dementia that affect people today are not, in the main, inherited. In fact, some of the major risk factors for dementia are modifiable, and so we can do many things to maximise our chances of avoiding the disease.

I have been studying and researching ageing and dementia for the best part of the last decade, and over this time there have been two revolutions. The first has been the discovery that vascular disease is a direct risk factor for Alzheimer's, with some researchers even claiming that Alzheimer's may in fact *be* a vascular disease of the brain. This has opened up the possibility that by optimising our vascular health, we may also decrease our risk of acquiring dementia. There are many facets to this intriguing idea, and so several chapters of this book are devoted to that topic.

The second revolution was a real showstopper, because the textbook wisdom that 'adults cannot create new brain cells' has been progressively and comprehensively overturned. We now know that the brains of adults naturally contain neural stem cells that are capable of producing new neurons. Many researchers—myself included—are trying to harness this process for the future treatment of Alzheimer's Disease.

However, this book is about *prevention*, because there is no truism in medicine more apt than 'an ounce of prevention is worth more than a pound of treatment'. Thus, early on in my research I became interested in the observation that dynamic, interesting people tended to develop dementia with much lower frequency. After surveying all the studies that had compared thousands of people with low and high mental activity, I was shocked to find almost a 50 per cent difference in favour of the mentally active. This connection between mental activity and dementia will therefore form the second half of this book.

For those without the time or inclination to read the book in its entirety, here's the bottom line: to best avoid dementia, keep your blood pressure in the normal range, and increase your level of diverse and complex mental activity, especially after retirement, whilst not forgetting about physical exercise and social engagement. There are, of course, no guarantees that any particular course of action will mean you don't develop the illness. But for concrete suggestions on how to optimise your chances of avoiding dementia, you will have to read on. This book may, in fact, be the first of its kind: the very act of reading it fulfils its dementia-preventing imperative.

At this point, I would like to give my warmest thanks to the family and friends who stoically read, commented on, and so improved this book: Mum and Dad, Vanessa, Mel P, and Sophia. Thank you, Kiran dearest, for both your feedback and encouragement and for your marvellous work with the healthy brain meal plan. I wish to thank especially my colleagues who contributed stand-alone sections to the book—Professor Henry Brodaty and Dr Adrienne Withall—and Professors Tony Jorm, Karen Cullen, Kuldip Sidhu, Sue Kurrle and Carl Cotman for direct and highly relevant quotations. Accolades to my mum (again) for her beautiful scientific illustrations. I would also like to single out Professor Perminder Sachdev for his peerless mentorship throughout my academic career. I owe him much.

My final message is for those inquisitive readers, or those who wish to refer a point of interest to their general practitioner. Given my background as a medico and psychologist, I felt it was important to back up some of the main points with at least one scientific reference. In the references you will therefore find the details of relevant scholarly medical articles. Any good library should be able to help you hunt down these articles, should you wish to learn more. Good luck and remember, *it's never too late to change your mind!*

CHAPTER 1

What is dementia?

What do we mean by 'dementia'?

Although most people feel they have an intuitive understanding of what **dementia*** is, I'm always surprised by the kind of responses they offer when pressed: 'Everyone gets dementia if you're old enough'; and 'Dementia means losing your mind/getting lost all the time/losing your memory/personality change.' While each of these ideas captures an element of truth, none is entirely correct. Surprisingly, this level of confusion is also mirrored in scientific circles, where every few years a presenter pops up at a conference and suggests that the standard definition is incomplete, inaccurate, or both.

Part of the problem is that dementia is actually the final step in a long series of biological events with many different possible

---

*Words in **bold** are defined in the glossary.

starting points. Take, for example, the kind of dementia associated with **Alzheimer's Disease** (AD). Researchers have been studying AD for over a century, and the characteristic pattern of brain changes is pretty well understood. As will be explored further in the next chapter, it is a *slow process* of gradual loss and shrinkage of brain cells that almost always starts in the same place in the brain, deep near the base of the skull.

Contrast that with the other main form of dementia in Western countries, **Vascular Dementia** (VaD). VaD begins with a stroke—a sudden loss of blood supply to a part of the brain, causing damage and death of brain cells. This type of dementia therefore starts with a *sudden injury* to the brain. Furthermore, the location of the stroke doesn't seem to be all that important; in some people a whole range of stroke locations and sizes can lead to dementia down the track.

So, two very different brain pathways can lead to the same outcome: dementia. What, then, do neurologists and psychiatrists mean when they refer to this condition?

In plain English, dementia is a noticeable and sustained decline in a person's mental faculties to the extent that day-to-day activities are severely affected, if not impossible. Dementia is therefore quite different from the kind of mental decline you and I may experience if, for example, we are delirious with a strong fever or severely dehydrated. This is because, in these conditions, our mental state has been affected by a *transitory* disturbance to our biological regulation. If we were to treat the infection with antibiotics, or commence intravenous fluids, our proper mental state would return. Unfortunately, at present, dementia is very much an untreatable, irreversible condition. In fact, dementia is invariably a *progressive* illness—once begun it gets worse, not better.

How does dementia differ from schizophrenia and depression?

The astute reader may ask, 'What, then, about the case of schizophrenia or depression; don't they count as dementia if a person's mental function is significantly degraded?' Interestingly, Emil Kraepelin, the German psychiatrist who in 1896 first systematically described schizophrenia, called it *dementia praecox*, or precocious dementia. He had noticed some clinical similarities between young people with schizophrenia and older people with dementia. We now know, however, that the differences outweigh the similarities. For example, the kinds of brain changes seen in schizophrenia are quite different from those seen in AD or VaD. Importantly, with proper medical care many individuals with schizophrenia are able to function at home and in society.

Depression is a bit trickier, because depression in an older person can present in a very similar way to dementia, so much so that the term **pseudodementia** is sometimes used. As you may know, the main feature of depression is an overwhelming feeling of sadness and hopelessness; so how can this be confused with dementia? It seems that depression can manifest in some older people quite differently than in younger adults, with social isolation and mental dysfunction more prominent than overt emotional pain. Why this is so is still not clear, but in my experience the stoic and laconic nature of the current older generation, many of whom lived through the Second World War, has something to do with it.

We all recognise that a person's mental function suffers when they are feeling down; however, with clinical depression the impact can be so great as to exclude normal day-to-day life. Depression can therefore mimic dementia in older people and potentially lead to an incorrect diagnosis. The implications of this are profound, because depression is a treatable condition. An incorrect diagnosis of dementia, instead of depression, can lead to a lot of unnecessary personal and family anguish, as well as prevent initiation of the appropriate treatment.

Another difficult issue can occur early in the dementia process when the individual becomes aware that the illness has begun, and of all that this entails. The discrepancy between what they are becoming, and what they were, can be very distressing. It is a human reaction to become depressed should you suspect that your mental faculties are significantly declining. Thus, the *co-occurrence* of dementia *and* depression is also quite possible, one exacerbating the other. For these reasons, the issue of depression should always be explored in individuals with a new dementia diagnosis.

The diagnostician can then be faced with a three-way choice: dementia alone, dementia plus depression, or atypical depression (pseudodementia). The situation can be so murky that sometimes the true state of affairs can only be established by a trial of antidepressant medication, or a wait-and-see approach. Fortunately, whether through the passage of time or the right treatment, the great majority of depression resolves, along with any associated mental impairment. This is therefore the cardinal difference between depression in an older person and true dementia: dementia does not resolve.

Cognitive domains and the diagnosis of dementia

So far, we have referred to mental function only in general terms. Yet, as we shall see, quite different brain diseases can lead to dementia, and so initially quite different **cognitive domains** can be affected. Cognitive domains are subsystems of mental function that combine to produce intelligent thought, action and speech. Neuropsychologists use any of a number of tests to gauge a person's strengths and weaknesses in different domains. Domains that will become important in our exploration of dementia in the next chapter include:

- **Memory**: our ability to store and recall information about events, people and places (episodic memory), knowledge (semantic memory) and sequential physical actions (procedural memory).

- **Attention**: our ability to focus concentration on a particular task at hand, or to split our concentration between two or more tasks at the same time.

- **Problem solving**: our ability to adapt to a new situation, overcome a challenge, and think of alternative solutions.

- **Inhibition**: our ability to suppress our initial 'instinctual' response, reflect on the situation, and then select the most appropriate response from a number of alternatives.

How big a problem is dementia?

Best estimates indicate that 220,000 Australians are affected by dementia. Direct medical costs for caring for these individuals total more than $3.2 billion a year. Incredibly, a recent survey by Pfizer has found that 47 per cent of adult Australians have a family member or friend with dementia.

Dementia is therefore now one of society's most pressing social and medical issues. In a historical context, it is clear why this has come to pass. In the United States at the turn of the nineteenth century, infection was the main killer of adults, whose average life span was just 47 years. Alzheimer's Disease and Vascular Dementia are mainly *late-onset* diseases, manifesting usually after the age of 60. Thus, at the start of the twentieth century, there were simply too few people in the right age range for dementia to be a major problem.

The last century has brought many revolutions, none less significant than in the health area, where the ready provision of clean water, sanitation and antibiotics has contributed enormously to longer life spans in developed countries. Furthermore, only 50 years ago, the average Australian life span was 70 years; today, it's 80. A large part of this increase has been due to the strides made in understanding and treating cardiovascular disease. Thirty years ago, for example, heart attack was the main killer of otherwise healthy individuals. Within the next 20 years, degenerative brain diseases, of which AD and VaD make up the overwhelming majority, will become our number one killer.

The reason for this is that the main risk factor for dementia is undisputed: increasing age. During our sixties, the frequency for dementia is less than 5 per cent, while in our eighties it jumps to 25 per cent. Hence, society's average life span will soon reach a stage where one in four individuals will develop dementia. This is particularly disturbing, as it means that many of us will die from a prolonged and insidious form of mental devastation, rather than suddenly 'falling off the perch'. It will also mean that the chances of our spending our final years in a nursing home, or with significant medical and nursing care at home, will become increasingly high.

Demographic predictions

There has been much said about the fact that the baby-boomer generation is getting older, entering into the dementia-risk age bracket of 60 years and above. Are dementia rates actually increasing, and should we be worried? The answer to both these questions is a resounding 'yes'.

The latest epidemiological data suggest that dementia rates are now starting to creep up. For example, the prevalence rate for dementia in Australia increased by 30 per cent during the period from 1993 to 2002. And the problem is set to become much worse, according to Professor Anthony Jorm of the ORYGEN Research Centre and Department of Psychiatry at the University of Melbourne. Professor Jorm, one of Australia's most respected mental health population researchers, says: 'The number of people with dementia has been steadily rising as the population ages. However, the peak is yet to come. When the baby boomers reach their eighties, there will be an epidemic of dementia unless we can do something to prevent it.'[1]

Economic modelling by Access Economics has found that if current rates of dementia were to translate to the bulging baby-boomer cohort, then annual spending on health as a proportion of gross domestic product would increase from 0.5 per cent to 3 per cent within a generation.[2] In short, the increased occurrence of dementia within the next 30 years entails the risk of bankrupting our governments. This is a real cause for concern. Extrapolation of current trends means that either care of individuals with dementia will become radically underserviced, or other important budgetary priorities will suffer.

This, then, seems to be the price of medical progress: we have become victims of our own success in treating mankind's major physical ailments. Is our collective destiny to succumb to an epidemic of 'brain failure', and financial calamity for the rest? Is the outlook really that bleak?

Fortunately, there are a number of reasons why that may not be so. First, there is always hope that an effective treatment will be discovered, and there are dozens of such treatments currently being trialled. Government and corporate sponsorship of basic and clinical dementia research is therefore critical to the continuation of our basic way of life. On this front, Australia is way behind the United States, and for no good reason. North

Americans spend on average $300 per citizen on dementia-related research each year; in Australia, the figure is $15.40. If you think this situation is unsatisfactory, write to your local Member of Parliament!

On a darker note, the current epidemic of obesity, diabetes and physical inactivity may actually mean that the average life span of Australians will begin to regress for the first time in 100 years. While this may result in fewer people developing dementia in the long term than otherwise, this is hardly a cause for celebration.

More positively, and irrespective of whether or not an effective treatment is found, we already have at our disposal a body of scientific knowledge for strategies we can all implement to reduce our risk of developing dementia. This is in fact the motivation for this book. We will cover seven emerging areas where protective links have been found. In general, two main themes will be explored: the link between physical health and dementia, and that between mental exercise and dementia. A basic principle in this area is that the sooner preventative changes are started, the better. So, I would urge the reader to consider the implications of action versus non-action, on both self and society, and *to start taking up these recommendations today!*

Before we move on to the science and art of dementia prevention, we need first to understand the similarities and differences between the two main forms of the illness, Alzheimer's Disease and Vascular Dementia. We will discuss what the dementia experience is like in each, and what researchers think is going on at the biological level.

CHAPTER 2

The main forms of dementia

Alzheimer's Disease

In 1906, Dr Alois Alzheimer described the case of one of his patients, a 51-year-old woman named Auguste D, as follows:

> ... An increasing weakness of memory became noticeable ...
> [S]he is ... completely disoriented. From time to time she says
> that she does not understand [what is happening to her]. ...
> Her memory is extremely disordered. If you show her some
> objects, she names them correctly, but shortly after she has
> forgotten everything.[1]

When he looked at the woman's brain under the microscope at post mortem, he noted a profusion of 'plaques', or abnormal collections of protein, throughout her brain. After Alzheimer observed this phenomenon in the brains of a number of individuals with similar clinical problems, he coined the term 'Alzheimer's Disease' (AD), which eventually entered into the medical lexicon in 1910.

What do we know about AD?

We now know a lot more about AD, its typical course and the types of associated brain changes. As Alzheimer himself observed, AD initially presents as a problem of memory. Typically, at the onset of the disease, the person consistently loses important items around the house (not just their keys or the remote control!), such that it becomes irritating and annoying, and starts to interfere with getting their daily chores done. Memory for directions becomes affected, and getting home from the local shops may start to become a challenge. Family members become concerned when the person starts to fail to recognise loved ones, and initially tries to conceal or minimise the error. Things then become increasingly worse. The person may have so much difficulty in finding the words they want that a normal conversation becomes impossible. Memory for distant and personally significant events, general knowledge for world events, and interpersonal connections crumble. Finally, the person's capacity to live safely becomes suspect. At this stage, formerly placid older people can become highly emotional, even violent and aggressive. They may also start to hear and see strange things. This is often the cue for the difficult family decision to start looking for a nursing home or supported living option. The life span of a person entering a nursing home with AD is typically less than five years. People with AD often finally succumb to a chest infection, due to their extended immobility and poor immune function, or their brain simply becomes unable to support their body's vital physiological functions.

We can see from this description that memory problems are a core feature of AD, particularly in its early stages. The disease then progresses to include planning and problem-solving impairments, followed by profound personality and inhibition difficulties. Psychotic episodes are also not unheard of in the later stages of AD. It is therefore clear that AD passes through a number of phases, initially manifesting as an **amnestic syndrome**, then as global cognitive impairment, and in the severe stages as an inability to carry out daily living tasks independently.

Diagnosing AD

The pattern of change described above is highly consistent in people with AD. For this reason, researchers tend to use formal criteria for the clinical diagnosis of the illness, so that when reports about its treatment and prognosis are made, we can be confident that we are talking about the same thing. Formal criteria for AD-dementia include:

- *Objective memory impairment, plus one or more cognitive domain difficulties.* Objective testing usually means having the person complete neuropsychological tests and comparing their performance with healthy individuals in the same age range.

- *A noticeable decline in mental function.* If a person has always performed poorly in a cognitive domain, then this doesn't count. However, if a person has declined from a truly superior cognitive range down to below average, then this represents an impairment *for that person.*

- *Cognitive difficulties are interfering with normal day-to-day function.* Many older people consider that their memory function is a problem, yet there is a poor relationship between such 'memory complaints' and objective memory performance. A better indicator is whether one's memory performance is starting to interfere with work, relationships, or getting things done around the house.

- *The problem is chronic and progressive.* The individual or family will have observed that the difficulties have been consistent for a number of months and seem to be getting worse.

- *Exclusion of transient medical causes.* As mentioned at the outset, there are a number of potential causes of a short-term decline in our mental faculties, including an infection, dehydration or a metabolic abnormality. Each needs appropriate assessment and exclusion before an AD diagnosis is considered.

From the description given above, it is clear that the impact of AD on the family, friends and caregivers of the affected person can be enormous. Professor Henry Brodaty, one of Australia's most respected AD clinicians and researchers, has led the field internationally in recognising the impact of dementia on family and carers. Carers for individuals with AD are themselves at increased risk for both medical and mental health problems. GPs and other health professionals therefore need to be vigilant, and look after the mental and physical health of individuals with loved ones affected by AD. For more information about this topic and how to best care for a loved one with dementia, see *In Focus* at the end of Chapter 6.

What causes AD?

The absolute bottom line is that we still don't know what causes AD. In the language of popular TV crime shows, we seem to have a good line-up of suspects who were in the general vicinity of the crime scene and who seem to have a motive; however, we can't find the weapon, let alone a smoking gun. In essence, we have circumstantial evidence, but a watertight case eludes us.

Orthodox theory for the development of AD puts the blame on those same abnormal plaques that Dr Alzheimer initially observed. This seems obvious at first glance: people become demented, we look in their brains and see masses of sticky, clumped-up protein that isn't normally present, and so we make the link. But what are these plaques made of, and how do they get there?

AD plaques are accumulations of a protein called **beta-amyloid** (or β-amyloid) in a concentrated, twisted form. In the rare *early-onset* version of AD, dementia tends to develop before the age of 50. Early-onset AD accounts for less than 5 per cent of AD overall, but it has been of much interest to scientists because specific genetic changes have been linked to it (see *In Focus* at the end of Chapter 5). We all, for example, carry 23 pairs of chromosomes in the nucleus of each of our cells, and changes in chromosome number 21 have been linked to abnormally high production of beta-amyloid. Specifically, some early-onset AD patients have an abnormal gene that produces aberrant levels of Amyloid Precursor Protein (APP), a protein that sits across the cell membrane of almost all brain cells (see Figure 4 in Chapter 6). APP is chopped up by enzymes within the cell to produce beta-amyloid, which is then secreted into the space between the brain cells (termed the **extracellular space**). This initial beta-amyloid can then change into a number of abnormally shaped aggregations and finally accumulate into the fibrillar beta-amyloid that we see under the microscope as plaques (see Figure 1 on page 34). These kinds of changes can also be seen in many individuals with Down Syndrome, who have three of chromosome 21 instead of two and are at much higher risk of developing early-onset AD.

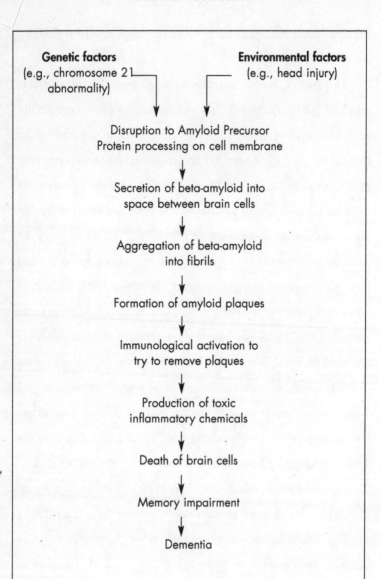

Figure 1 The classic 'amyloid hypothesis' for the development of dementia related to Alzheimer's Disease

The '**amyloid hypothesis**' for AD proposes either that fibrillar beta-amyloid is *directly* toxic to brain cells (**neurotoxic**), or that the presence of AD plaques causes activation of the brain's immune response, which—in an abortive attempt to clear the plaques—causes damaging inflammation and so is *indirectly* neurotoxic. It is important to keep in mind, however, that the overwhelming majority (greater than 95 per cent) of individuals with AD dementia have the *late-onset* version, which is not, as far as we know, predominately an inherited disease. Thus, we cannot be sure that those changes seen in the early-onset form have any relevance to what is going on in late-onset AD.

A competing hypothesis notes that while plaques are prevalent in the brains of people with AD, their distribution doesn't seem to match those brain areas suggested by the individual's symptoms. Given that AD typically begins with memory problems, it would seem natural that the area first affected would be the brain's memory centre, the **hippocampus**. The hippocampus (meaning *seahorse* in Greek) is an odd, folded-up sausage-shaped structure found deep near the base of the brain. It is critical to proper memory function in all mammals. We all have two hippocampi, a left and a right one, and they are highly interconnected.

However, when we look at the brains of older people with *early* AD, we don't tend to see beta-amyloid plaques in their hippocampus; rather, we see a different type of pathology called

neurofibrillary tangles (tangles). Tangles occur inside brain cells, as opposed to plaques, which are found outside in the extracellular space. Tangles are also comprised of an abnormally twisted protein—in this case, the tau-protein. Researchers have documented a typical pattern by which tangles start in the hippocampus, spread to the peripheral cortical areas of the brain, and then finally deposit in almost all brain areas. This pattern tends to replicate the pattern of symptoms seen in AD patients, with memory problems first, then global cognitive deficits, then brain failure.

By the 1980s, the stage was therefore set for one of the greatest medico-scientific stoushes of all time: the 'baptists' (beta-amyloid theory supporters) versus the 'tauists' (tau theory supporters)! For the dispassionate scientific observer, the level of vitriol and narrow-minded argument that reigned in this field for many decades was surprising, to say the least. But which camp was right? Unfortunately for everyone involved, it seems that the answer is 'probably neither'.

Part of the problem in the search for the root cause of AD is that the time line is quite long. Individuals with AD who are studied at autopsy have usually died with a severe form of the illness, and therefore we are seeing a snapshot of the disease in the last stages. There is a saying in the AD field: 'Tombstones tell you when a person died, but not from what cause.' Thus, the process of AD probably begins many years before the onset of symptoms, and still many more years before individuals come to autopsy. In this way, both plaques and tangles may be neurological 'tombstones', or end points, in a very different process begun decades earlier. Plaques and tangles may in fact be innocent bystanders, with the real perpetrator having fled the scene well before.

More worryingly, in those few studies that have directly examined the **correlation**—or strength of relationship—between either plaques or tangles and the cognitive status of the person prior to death, the link is very weak. Also, rather than compare the brains of AD patients with healthy brains, if we investigate the cognitive status of a whole population and look inside their brains following death, we see a very different picture. The Cognitive Function and Ageing Study,[2] based in Cambridge in the United Kingdom and one of the largest studies of its kind, found that more than 30 per cent of people with moderate to severe levels of either plaques or tangles were *not demented in life.*

What's going on, then, if the level of pathology has no clear relationship with the clinical condition? In brief, the brain is damned complicated! Without going into too much detail (as this topic could easily fill a book in itself), at least two important factors seem to be involved. First, our current understanding of the brain suggests that it is the highly complex and dynamic *connections between brain cells* that are responsible for the higher cognitive functions such as thinking, feeling and understanding that become disrupted in AD. Thus, if we look at the correlation between damage to **synapses** (connections between brain cells) and clinical status, we see a much clearer correlation: studies have shown that about 50 per cent of the clinical effects of AD can be explained by loss of synapses between cells.

A major recent turn in the AD research road has therefore been to focus specifically on when, how and if beta-amyloid or tangles disrupt synaptic function. This, in my opinion, is a welcome change. If, for example, clearing beta-amyloid from the brain has no effect on synaptic numbers, and therefore no effect on clinical condition, then pursuing this angle further as a treatment strategy is probably a waste of time and resources.

Second, the brain likes to obey Newton's third Law of Motion—every action has an opposite and equal reaction. So, when the brain suffers a small injury that knocks off some synapses, new synapses tend to grow back (a process called **synaptogenesis**). This happens not only in the local area, but elsewhere as well. Two hypothetical individuals could therefore have the same level of beta-amyloid or tangles in their brains, but one may have more *compensatory synaptogenesis* than the other, and so manifest fewer cognitive problems. Interestingly, as we shall see in Chapters 7 and 8, keeping mentally active throughout life may be one of the key ways to increase our brain's ability to compensate against early AD.

You may have noticed that when we talk about AD, we are actually talking about two things at two different levels: brain pathology and clinical symptoms. Pathology is those types of changes in the brain that were first noted by Dr Alzheimer a century ago, including beta-amyloid plaques and tangles. However, people are generally more interested in knowing how to prevent *dementia associated with AD*, a syndrome that starts with memory impairment and progresses to complete incapacitation. This is the level of clinical symptoms. There is obviously a big knowledge gap between these two levels, and we have just explored the idea that synaptic connections may be one important link between the two.

We will now turn to another form of dementia, Vascular Dementia, where the link between biological changes and the clinical syndrome is equally perplexing.

Vascular Dementia

What do we know about VaD?

Vascular Dementia is the most common cause of dementia in developing countries, while in developed countries it is the second most frequent cause after AD. VaD occurs in about 20–30 per cent of individuals in the first year after a **stroke**. A stroke is a medical emergency in which there is a sudden, temporary loss of blood supply to the brain. Two main forms of stroke occur, ischaemic and haemorrhagic stroke. In the former, blood vessels to the brain are blocked by either the steady accumulation of fatty deposits, or the sudden breaking up of a clot or fatty plaque upstream, which lodges in a narrow blood vessel and prevents adequate blood flow. Haemorrhagic stroke, on the other hand, involves a sudden breakage of a blood vessel so that blood supply downstream is inadequate.

The acute symptoms of stroke are mainly related to where in the brain the blood flow disruption has occurred; however, some common symptoms include a sudden loss of speech, weakness on one side of the face or body, intense pins and needles along one arm or leg, or a sudden loss of coordination or balance. In general, should any of the above symptoms occur in an older individual, the person should be considered as having had a stroke until proven otherwise and needs to be taken by ambulance to an emergency department for treatment as soon as possible. Part of the urgency is that there is good evidence that time-to-treatment is a major predictor of physical disability from a stroke.

VaD is, however, somewhat unrelated to the dramatic short-term effects of a stroke. It tends to creep up on people some months later, and up to a year after the event, when the physical effects have either resolved completely, or are stable and being managed with physiotherapy and occupational therapy. Like any dementia, the first symptoms are cognitive, and then progress to global mental dysfunction and an inability to carry out daily activities.

Research headed by Professor Perminder Sachdev of the Neuropsychiatric Institute in Sydney has shown that memory is typically *not* affected first. Rather, the most common initial cognitive problems in people with VaD are with problem solving, attention and inhibition.[3] Partners often report that the person is more emotional than normal; for example, stoic older men sometimes cry inexplicably. People with VaD have trouble focusing on a task at hand, so that complex tasks such as planning the week's budget become too difficult to perform. In general, the person seems to become more reckless and thoughtless, blurting out inappropriate statements and sometimes behaving socially unacceptably. The person's train of thought will wander, and conversation will take all sorts of frustrating meanderings, twists and turns. In general, psychiatric problems such as depression and apathy are more common in VaD than AD.

The progression of the disease is also less predictable than with AD. Some individuals will decline considerably in the first year and then remain relatively stable; others will gradually continue to worsen. We are still not sure what percentage of individuals with significant impairment one year after a stroke will continue to decline. In those whose condition worsens, placement in a nursing home is triggered by an inability to live safely at home; disorganisation and erratic behaviour sometimes contributing to truly squalid living conditions. In those that remain stable, the deficits can sometimes be accommodated by increased delivery of social services and the invaluable care of a loving partner or family member. Even in people with advanced VaD, long-term memory is relatively conserved. This means that brief stanzas of lucidity can occur, and provide precious glimpses of the 'true person' hidden behind the veil of disease. Prognosis for life expectancy after transfer to a nursing home is nevertheless poor, a number of years at most, and is perhaps even shorter than found in AD.

What causes VaD?

The initial stroke has an obvious role to play in VaD; however, as in most of clinical neuroscience, things aren't as simple as they first appear. First, neither the size of the stroke, nor its location, seems to have a strong relationship with the level of subsequent cognitive impairment. This therefore parallels the observation of weak clinical–pathological links as discussed in relation to AD. Second, there is a vast range of stroke types, distributions and severities, and yet all seem to predispose individuals to VaD. Finally, even though having an identified stroke is part of the formal criteria for VaD (which otherwise are almost identical to those for AD), this doesn't take into account the fact that many older individuals may have a stroke and not recognise or report it (i.e., a *silent* stroke) and subsequently develop the VaD syndrome.

This vast heterogeneity in the underlying cerebrovascular disease has led some theorists to ask whether the term 'Vascular Dementia' is itself misleading. Several alternatives have been advocated, including vascular cognitive impairment, cerebrovascular dementia, small vessel vascular dementia, leukoencephalopathy, and so forth. What is certain is that a spectrum of **cerebrovascular disease** surely exists. Even the brains of completely healthy, non-impaired individuals aged over 50 years will almost universally display some level of cerebrovascular disease, particularly around the **ventricles** in the middle of the brain. These unusual-shaped structures are filled with cerebrospinal fluid (CSF). CSF is composed essentially of water and bathes the entire brain and spinal cord.

Moving up the hierarchy, some individuals may have one or more tiny stroke areas (less than 1.5 centimetres in diameter), while others have more diffuse cerebrovascular disease of the white-matter areas. **White matter** in the brain refers to large bundles of **axons,** or communicating connections which link the brain cells together. These axons appear white to the naked eye because of the insulating fat surrounding them. Other individuals may have more intense white-matter disease, leading to a loss of large numbers of brain cells; and yet others may have areas of obvious dead tissue at the stroke site. While this spectrum lends itself to a notion of underlying severity, VaD appears to occur indiscriminately, sometimes in association with large strokes and other times with minimal white-matter disease.

So, how can this be? One of the more sophisticated hypotheses suggests that most, if not all, cerebrovascular disease shares a common disruption to the white-matter tracts that link deep structures in the brain with the frontal lobe. The frontal lobe, as the name suggests, is the large part of the cortex in the front half of the brain. Normal function of this brain area has been linked to attention, problem solving and inhibition—precisely those cognitive aspects that seem to be selectively vulnerable in VaD.

While dementia linked to AD initially manifests as an amnestic syndrome related to pathology in the hippocampus, VaD may at first be a *frontal syndrome* related to disruption of the proper function of the frontal lobe. Precisely what has gone wrong in the frontal brain region isn't clearly understood. Whether, for example, it is a loss of synapses, or damage to the white-matter connections between brain cells, is unknown. Or perhaps there is, in fact, no single true VaD entity, but rather a myriad of stroke-cognitive syndromes? Why a broad range of different types of blood-flow problems should all disrupt frontal lobe function in the same way is similarly unclear.

As in the case of AD, the brain seems to follow a natural imperative to maximise function, and so individuals will differ in their ability to compensate for the injury caused by the stroke. Also as in AD, complex mental activity appears to be a major determinant of long-term cognitive outcome following a stroke, with compensatory synaptogenesis emerging as a general principle in understanding the outcome following *any brain injury*. More will be said on this topic in Chapters 7 and 8.

The final, and perhaps most fascinating, twist to this tale is the ever-growing body of scientific reports linking cerebrovascular disease directly with AD pathology. This research, which suggests that by treating and correcting vascular risk factors we can reduce our risk for *both* Vascular Dementia *and* Alzheimer's Disease, is one of the most exciting areas of dementia research to emerge in the past decade. We will be exploring these ideas in some detail in Chapters 3–7.

IN FOCUS   A case study: 'Fish 'n' Chips'

I met Mr G for the first time in the Emergency Department in the early hours of the morning. He came in with a broken hip, a bewildered look on his face, and hot chips in his ears. He was dressed in pyjamas, a dressing gown and those tartan-patterned slippers of which only older people are fond. It was very difficult to get any real information at that stage from Mr G, apart from 'You're not an Itie are you?' or 'Nick off, will you, or I'll do you in!'.

He was in obvious pain, and dehydrated from the blood leaking into his fracture—all suitable reasons for an older individual to present dazed, confused and disoriented. After attending to these more pressing needs, we embarked on the task of working out who he was, and why he had come to be in Emergency. After some time and a lot of TLC, Mr G settled down. He told us his name, gave us a range of different credible street addresses, and explained that he had felt like some 'fish and chips'.

By the mid-morning Mr G's very worried-looking family had turned up, led by his son. It was at this point that the diagnosis of dementia related to Alzheimer's Disease became quite obvious. Mr G's son explained that the family had been trying to convince his dad to move to a supervised living home 'for a while'. They explained that Mr G had worked as a milkman and then as newspaper shop owner, and had served his country in the Second World War. He had been a regular, lovable grandfather; but then, a couple of years ago, he had started to suffer from increasing word-finding difficulties. According to the son, this became much worse after Mr G's wife passed away. He began to repeat questions and phrases a lot, and to forget prearranged engagements and family events.

About two months ago, family members were contacted by the police. Mr G had been found wandering and 'lost'. This set off the alarm bells, and they realised that he was probably suffering from dementia. Mr G must have had a very forceful personality because, even then, he refused to be moved out of his home. The family started to rotate daily responsibility for visits, to make sure that he was eating sufficiently, was properly dressed, showered and so forth. According to them, while some parts of his personality seemed to remain, mainly his legendary stubbornness, the 'real person' seemed to have slowly vanished. He did at least seem to recognise their faces, if not their names or significance.

From what we worked out, Mr G had become hungry in the middle of the night, and had simply walked straight out of his house, stumbled, and broken his hip. We never figured out how he happened to find hot chips at that time of the night.

Sadly, Mr G's penchant for a midnight snack proved his demise. He died within a week from complications related to his orthopaedic surgery. The family were devastated, as one would expect, wondering whether things would have turned out differently if they had been more decisive with their father. I still wonder if perhaps fate had dealt a kinder blow.

CHAPTER 3

A *healthy heart means a healthy brain*

The link between blood flow and brain function

Pound for pound, no other part of the human body uses more energy at rest than the brain. Brain cells need to communicate with other brain cells through synaptic connections of stunning complexity. In order for these signals to be transferred, the message is sent in the form of a neural code. This code is 'written' in the language of *frequency*: charged pulses travel down the neuron's axonal cables and are then transmitted between cells at the **synaptic junction**. It turns out that transmitting messages in this way is, in energy terms, very expensive. Nature's engineering may be beautiful, but it is also high maintenance, something that is readily apparent by how 'muddy' our thinking becomes if we're low on sugar.

Think of an individual brain cell as a small battery. By pumping more positively charged molecules out of the cell than are allowed to drift back in, a *potential difference*—or voltage—is generated across the cell's outer membrane. Frequency messages perturb this voltage and allow the perturbation to propagate along the cell's long axonal cable like a wave. That's how the motor command to wriggle your toes gets from the top of your head to the tip of your foot in less than 50 milliseconds!

The potential difference across the membrane of just a single cell can be measured, and remarkably is in the order of 70 millivolts. That's 70 millivolts of potential energy across a distance as tiny as 6 nanometres. (A nanometre is one millionth of a millimetre.) A neuron the size of your average television set would carry a potential difference of 200 *megavolts*; this is astounding given that a lightning bolt is estimated to form when the potential difference between land and sky reaches about 50 megavolts! Some scientists have speculated that the humble neuron may well represent the greatest concentration of voltage anywhere on Earth. In order to maintain such a high voltage across the membrane of each and every cell in the brain, trillions upon trillions of tiny ionic pumps need to work overtime moving charged molecules out of the cell. It is these ionic pumps that take up the lion's share of the brain's energy requirements.

In the neural world, therefore, we burn glucose for all sorts of reasons, but the most important is to keep a high, steady and reliable voltage across the membrane of each of the brain's 100 billion cells. Why? So that, when required, each cell can communicate with other cells in a deeply mysterious process that allows regulation of our basic body functions, wakefulness, emotions, thoughts and fantasies.

It should be apparent, therefore, how crucial a good, clean supply of energy is for proper brain function. Equally, like any engine, each brain cell needs to get rid of its waste products. Each brain cell therefore needs a steady supply of glucose and oxygen to combust, and to be able to get rid of carbon dioxide (CO_2). The only way to do this is via the brain's blood supply, or in technical terms the **cerebrovasculature**.

Two big *internal carotid arteries* feed the brain by travelling up the neck after branching off from the *aorta*, the main hosepipe that leaves the heart full of oxygen- and glucose-rich blood. After entering the brain proper, the internal carotids then divide into three main arteries. These then branch into smaller arterioles, which in turn branch into countless fine wispy capillaries. Each brain cell receives its supply of glucose, oxygen, vitamins and other essential compounds by being in direct proximity to a tiny network of nutrient-rich capillaries. Then the process is reversed. Tiny venules pick up the waste products and leftovers, which drain into the larger veins. These larger veins then collect to form the main outgoing jugular vein, which dumps its depleted blood into the right side of the heart. This inferior, dark and nutrient-poor blood is rejuvenated by passing through the lungs, and so enters the left side of the heart re-oxygenated and re-energised to start the cycle once again.

You don't have to be a brain scientist to work out that any serious interruption of proper blood flow and nutrients is going to be bad for brain function! Yet, it's only in the last 10–15 years that serious attention has been paid to the link between cardiac health and mental health. Quite simply, the results have been revolutionary.

Vascular health and Vascular Dementia

Let's start with the obvious. Vascular Dementia is, by definition, a type of dementia that develops in about one in four people after a stroke of some sort. VaD is also the second most common form of dementia in developed countries, and the most common in developing nations. So, in order to prevent VaD we need to prevent strokes occurring in the first place. And here is the first link between the brain and the heart: most of the same pathology associated with *cardiovascular* disease is also implicated in *cerebrovascular* disease because, in fact, it is all part of the same vascular system.

The fatty cholesterol deposits, plaques, clots and inflammatory processes that are now well known to cause heart disease, angina and heart attacks also develop a bit further upstream in the brain's major blood vessels. When a major heart vessel occludes with a dislodged plaque, we feel the pain of a **myocardial infarction** (*heart attack*). When the same thing happens in the middle cerebral artery of the brain, we suddenly can't speak or walk or comprehend the world. This is because the segment of the brain that controls these functions has lost its energy supply and has begun to die. It's no coincidence that the medical term for a stroke is **cerebral infarction**.

It follows that the best way to avoid Vascular Dementia is to avoid having a stroke in the first place, which requires us to do our best to avoid vascular disease in general. And we already know how to do this! Even the most sanguine person when it comes to their own health will recognise some of the five most important vascular risk factors: smoking, obesity, bad **cholesterol**, diabetes and high blood pressure.

So, in order to maximise your chances of avoiding Vascular Dementia you need to get your abdominal fat down, do regular exercise, and check your cholesterol, blood sugar and blood pressure. We will dedicate an entire chapter to some of these *modifiable risk factors*, because their link with dementia goes beyond the obvious. Let's just make the point here that if you are fit and healthy in your middle-age years, your risk of having a stroke in later life will be halved, and so you will be *less likely* to develop Vascular Dementia.

Urban myth: Smoking prevents dementia

At this juncture, we need to dismiss a commonly held misperception, which is that somehow smoking prevents people from developing dementia. Some earlier studies had indeed shown that, in very old age, there seemed to be lower rates of dementia in those that had smoked during their life. A problem with studies of the very old, however, is a phenomenon called the 'survivor effect'. People aged in their nineties and upward are obviously very hardy individuals, and may carry a range of advantageous genes for longer life that make them more resistant to cardiovascular disease *and* dementia. Since we know that smoking typically kills people prematurely, what could have been happening? It's possible that smokers with 'survivor genes'—the kind of people who smoke, drink and do all the wrong things, yet just keep on going—could have been positively selected through the dropout of their 'normal' smoking buddies who died when aged in their fifties and sixties.

In any case, the answer is now much clearer. Professor Kaarin Anstey of the Australian National University selected 19 high-quality population studies that best avoided the survivor effect and tracked the outcomes over a number of years.[1] It turns out that older people who smoke have an 80 per cent increased risk of developing dementia, compared with those who have never smoked. So, just as smoking is a terrible risk factor for heart disease and heart attack, so it is for stroke and dementia. Clearly, if you wish to avoid dementia you shouldn't smoke.

Vascular health and Alzheimer's Disease

We have seen the direct link between cardiovascular disease and Vascular Dementia, but what about cardiovascular disease and Alzheimer's Disease? This is one of the hottest and most controversial topics in the dementia area.

In Chapter 2 we introduced the orthodox theory for how amyloid plaques—the abnormalities that form one of the cardinal features of Alzheimer's Disease—are formed. You will notice that at no stage was cerebrovascular disease (CVD) implicated in the so-called amyloid cascade. This old-school kind of thinking is now being challenged, and on a number of fronts. Let's start with population trends.

It is now a well-established finding that individuals with a greater number of cardiac risk factors (smoking, hypertension, diabetes, hypercholesterolemia, and so on) are also at increased risk of developing Alzheimer's Disease (and Vascular Dementia, of course). *But how much more at risk?* Studies suggests that those with many cardiac risk factors, compared to those with one or no risk factors, have about two to three times the risk of developing dementia in later life. What's more, having a stroke increases your risk of developing not only VaD, but AD as well, further suggesting a link between poor vascular health and Alzheimer's Disease.

Let's now turn to the biological level. Experiments have been done in mice genetically modified to produce human variants of amyloid plaques in order to determine the effect of reducing the amount of blood going to a particular part of the brain. These animals are therefore a kind of simulation of AD and stroke put together. The studies have shown that more amyloid protein begins to be secreted into the space around the cells that are **ischemic** (reduced blood supply).

This was quite an exciting finding, because for the first time there was a clue that the dynamics of blood supply may be involved in the formation of amyloid plaques, the main pathological feature of Alzheimer's Disease. A number of different groups and researchers have now shown similar results using various different animal models. Yet rodent models remain a relatively poor simulation of what happens in the human brain. We therefore need to turn to evidence from human research.

A major study of hundreds of brains of elderly donors from communities around the United Kingdom found that dementia was most commonly associated with the coexistence of *both* Alzheimer's pathology (plaques and tangles) *and* cerebrovascular disease. This is both instructive and perplexing. What it teaches us is that so-called pure cases of Alzheimer's Disease are actually not all that common in real life. More common is the existence of both diseases at the same time, so-called **mixed dementia**.[2] Yet, it doesn't reveal whether CVD causes AD, or AD causes CVD, whether there is a third common element to both processes, or if these are simply two independent processes occurring at the same time. It would be fair to say that most traditionalists in the area believe these are independent processes, but I am more convinced that CVD bears an intimate relationship with the development of AD—and therefore with AD-related dementia.

Associate Professor Karen Cullen of the University of Sydney has added more weight to the argument by looking at things from a new angle. Rather than simply noting whether an individual's post-mortem brain sample had AD pathology or CVD pathology, her approach was to determine whether there was a *spatial* or *topographic* relationship between the two. Dr Cullen and her team first used a histological staining technique that highlights areas of iron deposition when a sample of brain tissue is viewed under the microscope. Iron is seen in the brain as a breakdown product of haemoglobin, the key oxygen-carrying protein in the blood. One only sees iron in the brain *outside* of blood vessels if there has been a leakage of blood, such as in the case of a microbleed. Microbleeds occur when there is a tiny rupture of the fine capillaries that feed individual **neurons**. Microbleeds are essentially asymptomatic, meaning we never realise when they occur, and their pathological significance remains uncertain.

However, what Dr Cullen and her team did next was very

clever. Using the same thin sections of brain that they had marked for iron, they also stained the tissue for beta-amyloid and so were able to visualise the amyloid plaques, which are the hallmark of AD. You can now imagine that we have two sets of pictures of the same landscape: one has all the microbleeds highlighted, the other all the AD plaques. By superimposing the two images, the question of whether they tend to overlap could be addressed. The results were quite definitive. Microbleeds and AD plaques coincide in 'brain space' far more often than could be expected by chance alone (see Figure 2). Very often, in fact, a microbleed was noted at a branch point of a capillary with an AD plaque sitting directly on top of it.

Dr Cullen's hypothesis is that capillary branches are points of vulnerability and that with age the capillary walls become frail, leading to increased microbleeds. With blood leaking into the space between brain cells, rather than to the proper spot for transfer of oxygen, glucose and other nutrients, the neurons in the vicinity become ischemic. It is this very localised 'mini-ischemia' that is suggested to start the amyloid cascade that then develops into AD.

This is quite a revolutionary idea, because it puts development of plaques very late event in the sequence and promotes microvascular disease as the 'prime mover'. Adding to the argument is the observation that microbleeds first begin to develop in the hippocampus, an area first affected in AD

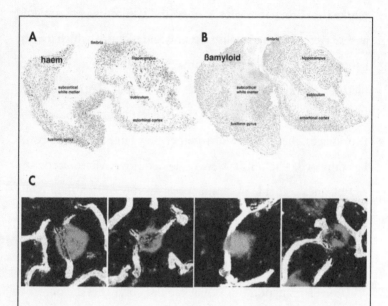

Figure 2 Distribution of iron-rich deposits and beta-amyloid plaques in the human brain. Panels A and B show a piece of human brain sliced in the same direction as if you were to wave your hand from above your brow down past your nose to below your chin. In general, the distribution of iron-rich deposits (A) closely resembles that for beta-amyloid (B). It is particularly intense in the hippocampus, the known focal point for AD. The three panels beneath (C) show an extreme close-up, with amyloid plaques labelled in dark grey and capillaries in light grey. It is clear that some plaques tend to form on top of capillary branch points.

Source: Parts A and B © 2005 Elsevier Inc. Part C, courtesy of Dr Karen M. Cullen. From Karen M. Cullen, Zoltan Kosci and Jonathan Stone, 'Microvascular pathology in the ageing human brain: Evidence that senile plaques are sites of microhaemorrhage, *Neurobiology of Ageing*, Elsevier, December 2006.

dementia. Dr Cullen explains as follows why microbleeds seem to develop first in this part of the brain, which is vital for memory, even though we rarely see strokes in this area:

> I suspect that the hippocampus has the most tangled and complex vascular supply of any part of the brain. If you look at the vascular structure in this area, it is very convoluted with many kinks, twists and branches. We are in the process of scientifically characterising this level of tortuosity, to use the technical term. I think it is because of this heightened tortuosity and branching that the hippocampus is particularly susceptible to microbleeds and therefore the development of Alzheimer plaques.[3]

If this idea turns out to be correct, the implications will be enormous. First, the traditional beta-amyloid cascade hypothesis will be dead and buried. Amyloid plaques may in the end have no inherent toxicity themselves, but may rather represent an incidental event at the end of a long series of biological changes; or they could even be a type of protective response by the brain to the ischemia that started the process in the first place. Second, the focus of anti-AD dementia drugs will need to turn to combating microvascular disease rather than plaque formation.

However, we are still some way from these heady conclusions. This is because, even with the benefit of the overlapping maps showing microbleeds and AD plaques in proximity, it is still only a snapshot in time. There is no way of getting around this problem when working with human post-mortem tissue. So, again the problem becomes a chicken-and-egg one: are the microbleeds causing AD plaques or vice versa, or neither?

Anti-hypertensives for the prevention of dementia

In order to try and grapple with this issue of *causality*, we need to turn to human clinical trials. In medical science, it is only through a rigorously conducted **randomised control trial** (RCT) that we can determine, finally, whether Factor X *causes* a change in Outcome Y. It turns out that one of the strongest risk factors for microvascular disease is hypertension. Fortunately, we now have the results of a number of large-scale RCTs of anti-hypertensives in elderly individuals with long-term follow-up. While these trials were aimed at determining whether controlling high blood pressure led to protection from heart attacks and stroke, the rate of development of dementia has also been analysed.

Six major RCTs have examined the link between treatment of hypertension and subsequent development of dementia or the rate of cognitive decline.[4] The good news is that across all these trials, effects were in the right direction. Those on anti-hypertensives tended to have better cognitive or dementia outcomes than those on a placebo after a number of years. The less good news was that not all of these trends reached a statistical threshold. Three trials showed a statistically *insignificant* decrease in dementia incidence of between 7 per cent and 16 per cent. Results from the other three trials, however, were more encouraging. The PROGRESS (Perindopril Protection Against Recurrent Stroke Study) trial found that those on hypertension medication had a statistically significant reduction in dementia with recurrent stroke of 34 per cent. Similarly, the HOPE (Heart Outcomes Prevention Evaluation) trial found that the rate of cognitive decline in those with a previous stroke was reduced significantly (by 41 per cent). Hence, treatment of hypertension in older individuals is very likely to reduce the chances of developing Vascular Dementia.

But what about Alzheimer's Disease? It may be surprising, but the only large-scale RCT to show evidence of prevention of Alzheimer's Dementia using *a medication of any sort* has come from a study of anti-hypertensives. The European SYST-EUR (Systolic Hypertension in Europe Trial) trial involved 4,695 individuals over the age of 60 who had high blood pressure to start with. The main anti-hypertensive medication that was tested was nitrendipine. Originally, the SYST-EUR trial was scheduled to run for four years; however, it was stopped after only two years because the stroke results were so emphatic: those on medication had 28 per cent fewer strokes than those on a placebo. Those in the treatment group also suffered 15 per cent fewer serious cardiac events. More importantly, the incidence of dementia was also reduced by 50 per cent in the treatment group—including reductions in *both* Alzheimer's Dementia *and* Vascular Dementia. These statistically significant results were then confirmed in a separate follow-up report four years later.

We therefore have strong evidence from the SYST-EUR trial that medical treatment of hypertension in the elderly can reduce the development of dementia, both Vascular and Alzheimer's. In an ideal world, all six trials would have replicated the same effect, but medical science—and especially clinical neuroscience— rarely offers such neatly packaged answers. What is important is that the trends are all in the right direction and at least one major, multi-centre and rigorously conducted trial has confirmed the result. So finally, after almost 100 years of research into dementia, we have an effective medical weapon in our armory—good old blood pressure tablets!

You would think that the media would be all over this finding, and that every older person with even the mildest case of high blood pressure would be at the pharmacist's door for their anti-hypertensives, right? For reasons beyond me, this is not the case. Few GPs, let alone interested lay people, seem aware that anti-hypertension medication can reduce the incidence of dementia. According to one study, up to 80 per cent of Australians are unaware of the links between hypertension and dementia. One reason for this may be that, at the time of these trials in the late 1990s, we had no way of explaining the link between anti-hypertensive medication and reduced dementia, particularly Alzheimer's Dementia.

Now there is a growing theoretical and experimental body of work linking cerebrovascular disease and Alzheimer's pathology. This, of course, includes the microbleed hypothesis, but also other ideas of how anti-hypertensives may be effective. For example, one study of rats that spontaneously develop hypertension found that the neural loss which normally accompanies this condition was avoided by treatment with the same class of anti-hypertensives as nitrendipine used in the SYST-EUR trial (**calcium channel blockers**). Furthermore, this neuroprotective effect was seen even in rats where the dose of calcium channel blocker was so mild that it had no effect on the animal's blood pressure. Hence, the results seen in human trials may be related either directly to positive effects on blood pressure, and thus on cerebrovascular disease, or to a protective effect on brain cells. Both types of mechanisms are compelling, and to my mind are not mutually exclusive. Keeping your blood pressure under control may help prevent dementia by both avoiding stroke and cerebrovascular disease and by directly protecting one's neurons.

Another reason for the lack of interest by the media may be that the whole area of blood pressure control in late life is confusing. High blood pressure in one's middle-age years is linked to a higher rate of both Vascular and Alzheimer's Dementia some 20–30 years later. This has now been shown in a number of large epidemiological follow-up studies. Yet, paradoxically, blood pressure in individuals who *already* have dementia is commonly lower than normal. One study has found that in those individuals who developed dementia in their eighties, their blood pressure was elevated up to 70 years of age, then started to drop and was even *hypotensive* in the couple of years preceding the onset of the dementia.

The technical aspects of measuring blood pressure in the elderly are also less straightforward than in younger individuals. Blood pressure tends to vary more in the elderly, especially depending on the person's body position. The difference between the low (diastolic) and high (systolic) values also tends to diverge more. Blood pressure is a complex measure affected by a number of factors, not least the 'white coat' phenomenon where people become anxious in the presence of their doctor, leading to artificially high blood pressure readings.

A result of all these issues is that GPs and physicians commonly question the wisdom of treating high blood pressure in the elderly. They doubt the cost–benefit ratio of starting an anti-hypertensive in later life, with little presumed gain and the risk of side effects or complications such as falls due to reduced blood pressure. These assumptions now mean that in the United States around 75 per cent of individuals over 80 years of age have untreated systolic hypertension.[5] In my opinion, this is a sad state of affairs. Clearly, normalising blood pressure in the elderly improves their general health outcomes, such as incidence of heart attack and stroke. There is also a *high likelihood* that proper control of blood pressure—in both mid-life and later life—reduces one's risk of developing Vascular Dementia *and* Alzheimer's Dementia. I recommend that all individuals have their GP monitor their blood pressure regularly, and take appropriate steps if it is above normal values. It's good for your heart as well as for your brain.

The cerebrovascular–Alzheimer continuum

A concept that emerges from this chapter is that cerebrovascular disease and Alzheimer's Disease may lie on the same continuum. At extreme ends, there are those cases of 'pure' CVD or AD that the classical neuropathologists often like to assume are the gold standard. In reality, any older person's brain will most likely manifest elements of both diseases.

Beyond this superficial coincidence, there is emerging research showing that CVD may be more intimately related to the development of AD. I will add two more fascinating results to underline this argument. Dr Giulio Maria Pasinetti, of Mount Sinai Medical Center in the United States, tested the effects of hundreds of commonly used medications on rats engineered to produce the human variant of amyloid plaques. He and his team found that no less than seven different types of anti-hypertensives reduced the development of amyloid-plaques in the brains of these animals and improved their performance on memory tests. While extrapolation of this result to the human situation is still premature, the classical beta-amyloid cascade hypothesis has no way of accounting for this finding. At some level, the vascular and beta-amyloid pathways seem to interact.

Next, at the main radiological conference held in North America in late 2007, brain imaging evidence was presented that high blood pressure in older individuals paradoxically *reduces* blood flow to the hippocampus, which is that part of the brain critical to memory and first affected in AD. It is hence conceivable that high blood pressure causes localised ischemia in the hippocampus, which then, through microbleeds and other vascular pathology, could kick off the amyloid cascade towards AD. This idea appeals because it combines both vascular and AD pathology, and the memory-loss symptoms of early AD dementia into one 'neat' story. This is a hypothesis that I suspect will receive increasing attention in the coming years.

Beyond these mechanistic speculations, the most convincing evidence for the CVD–AD continuum is that treatment of a very specific vascular problem—hypertension—most probably reduces the risk for both Vascular and Alzheimer's Dementia. The only way this could occur is by vascular disease and AD sharing some common element. We are therefore ready to learn our first lesson and make our first recommendation.

Lesson #1. *There is a strong probability that keeping blood pressure in the healthy range reduces your risk of dementia.*

For an explanation of what 'strong probability' actually means, see the *In Focus* panel at the end of this chapter. A healthy heart means a healthy brain. Therefore, all the same recommendations for avoiding cardiovascular disease apply to the brain as well.

Recommendation #1. *Make it a goal to maintain a normal blood pressure, and check it annually.*

How do I do this?

- Get your blood pressure (BP) checked by your GP. Insist on a standing, as well as sitting and lying, BP on two separate occasions, preferably on both arms.
- If your BP is too high, start with lifestyle changes. Then, if required, trial medication in consultation with your GP.
- Lifestyle change includes losing weight. The healthy weight range is a Body-to-Mass Index (BMI) of less than 25, and a waistline less than 94 centimetres for men and 80 centimetres for women. Your GP can assess these and provide more information.

- Exercise. The American College of Sports Medicine and the American Heart Association updated their exercise recommendations at the end of 2007. Their recommendations may surprise.
  - *Individuals aged less than 65 years* should do 30 minutes of moderate exercise at least *five times a week.* Moderate exercise means at least a brisk walk. In addition, at least 20 minutes a week should be devoted to resistance exercises such as weights, push-ups or sit-ups.
  - *For those aged 65 years or older,* 30 minutes of exercise three to four times a week is recommended. Moderate exercise in this case is anything that feels not too strenuous, not too light. In addition, strengthening exercises for the main muscle groups are recommended on two non-consecutive days of the week. Regular stretching and balance exercises are also suggested for the prevention of falls.
  - See Chapter 8 for recreational pastimes that are good for the heart, body and mind.
- Stop smoking.
- Have your cholesterol checked and aim for a healthy range (see Chapter 5).
- Have your blood sugar checked and aim for a healthy range (see Chapter 4).
- Maintain a healthy balanced diet, with plenty of brain- and heart- food (see Chapter 4).

IN FOCUS   A practical scale for understanding medical 'certainty'

You may have noticed that doctors and medical scientists hardly ever use the words 'definitely' or 'guaranteed'. Almost every statement is qualified (like this one) by 'perhaps', 'maybe' or 'likely'! Consider it a natural cautiousness because, if one thing is definitively guaranteed in medicine, it is that there are no certainties.

We therefore need a practical language for dealing with degrees of certainty. Throughout this book I have endeavoured to use the following terms when summarising the effect of one factor on a particular outcome. These terms are based on a hierarchy of certainty—each higher level needs a more stringent or more consistent factual basis than the previous.

For example, earlier it was suggested that there was a *strong probability* that keeping blood pressure normal throughout life reduces one's risk for dementia. By using the scale below, it is clear that a statement of *strong likelihood* infers three main levels of evidence: consistent epidemiological research; a plausible biological theory with related support from experiments; and supportive but not universally consistent evidence from clinical trials. In the dementia area, that's about as good as it gets.

Beginning with the strongest level of certainty and ending with the weakest ...

1. *Definitive effectiveness/Certain causal agent:*

   This infers that a series of randomised clinical trials (RCTs) *all agree* that agent X has a positive effect on outcome Y. Along with this is, epidemiological reports consistently link X with Y, and there is a plausible biological theory with experimental support for the mode of action (i.e., how X affects Y). Unfortunately, in the dementia area there is no intervention with this class of medical certainty.

2. *Strong possibility/Strong likelihood:*

   Consistent epidemiological links along with a plausible biological theory with experimental evidence for the mode of action. Results of RCTs are mixed, with at least one major clinical trial supporting the intervention.

3. *Probable/likely:*

   Generally consistent epidemiological links, but not entirely so. Some biological hypotheses for a mode of action and some experimental evidence, but also not entirely consistent. No positive results from RCTs.

4. *Potential:*

   Individual epidemiological or biological reports with no clear consistency or plausible theory to account for it. No RCT evidence of any nature.

CHAPTER 4

Food for thought

Food is special. It not only nourishes and sustains us, but can also invoke strong emotions of delight and become intimately associated with vivid memories. The right sorts of foods can also keep our heart—and therefore our brain—healthy, which is a double blessing. Yet, food also has a dark side—for it can seduce us into obesity and diabetes, which, apart from ruining our general health, may also have more direct links with the development of dementia. In this chapter we will review the links between food and dementia risk—the good, the bad and the ugly.

The elephant in the room: The ageing process and dementia

In 2006, Professor Carol Brayne of the University of Cambridge in the United Kingdom wrote an influential scholarly article on the risk factors for dementia titled 'The Elephant in the Room'. What she meant by this was that, while much attention is given to how we can modify and change risk factors for dementia such as hypertension, smoking, education, and so forth, the simple ageing process dwarfs these by a factor of more than 7:1. Consider this: during our sixties, the likelihood of our getting dementia is 1/20 (5 per cent); in our seventies it is 1/10 (10 per cent); and by the time of our eighth decade it has jumped to 1/4 (25 per cent). In other words, our risk of developing dementia seems to more than double every ten years. Why is this? If only we knew.

Our bodies and our brains change in countless different ways as we get older, and any of these changes may be at fault. The increased rate of stroke and cerebrovascular disease with age is one potential reason, but it is certainly not the whole story. At least we can exclude a simple explanation—it is *not* because we simply lose brain cells as we get older. This idea has been around for a while, but over the last ten years the more sophisticated and accurate techniques used for counting and measuring brain cells have shown that this idea simply doesn't stand up to scrutiny. All the best evidence suggests that the ageing process isn't normally accompanied by the loss of a significant number of brain cells.

Given that the passage of time is such a dominant risk for dementia, it stands to reason that if we first try to understand the fundamental changes associated with brain ageing, and then attempt to reverse these changes, we should be able to avoid dementia. Unfortunately, while this may make intuitive sense, it is easier said than done.

The oxidation theory of ageing

One of the oldest and most well-worn theories of biological ageing invokes the concept of cellular **oxidation**. Put a slice of apple on the kitchen counter, and it will turn brown within a few hours through the process of oxidation. The term 'oxidation' refers to the transfer of charge from oxygen-related molecules to cell proteins and other large cellular compounds, which ends up changing their biological properties.

Yet, every second of every day the cells in our bodies oxidise perfectly well without ill-effect because of an elegant system of counter-oxidisation, or natural **antioxidants**. However, this balance is finely poised. Almost any stress, infection, injury or damage to our body's cells will lead to an imbalance of oxidants over antioxidants and, consequently, to a build-up of nasty super-oxidants called free radicals. Free radicals are biological vandals, ruining almost anything they touch. Fortunately for us, once the stressor, pathogen or injury is removed, our body's marvellous recuperative systems also begin clearing any remaining free radicals.

The Australian Nobel-prize winning medical scientist Sir Macfarlane Burnet said in 1974 that oxidation was central to the ageing process and that finding ways to counteract this process would prolong the human life span and prevent the development of age-related diseases such as Alzheimer's Disease.[1] Indeed, you could fill a small library with the volume of research articles illustrating how ageing increases any one of a myriad of oxidation markers in almost any cell in the human body. Similarly, it is impossible to argue against the idea that as we get older our brain cells also appear to show signs of oxidative stress.

But does this oxidative stress have any consequences for brain function and dementia? Here the picture quickly fades to black. Unquestionably, brain samples from individuals who died with Alzheimer's Dementia have higher levels of oxidative stress than other individuals of the same age. But again the question arises, what came first? Does oxidative stress drive the AD process, or is it simply a sign of cells under attack? Clinical trials of antioxidants could therefore be really helpful by clarifying the relationship between oxidation and dementia. And they have been. Against all the odds, antioxidants seem to have *no* role in either the prevention or treatment of dementia.

Is there a 'cure' for ageing?

Antioxidants

Any grandmother worth her salt will know the trick of squeezing a bit of lemon juice on apple slices in order to keep them from turning brown. In this case, the ascorbic acid (vitamin C) in the lemon juice acts as a highly effective antioxidant. If only the brain was so simple! Yet, we have believed it to be. Major clinical trials have tested the effects of vitamin E (a more powerful antioxidant than vitamin C) and monoamine oxidase inhibitors (MAOIs, such as selegiline) for the prevention of AD dementia and also as a possible therapeutic. All have been spectacular failures. Individuals treated with high doses of vitamin E exhibited no more benefits than their antioxidant-less counterparts.

What's more, excessive amounts of vitamin E can actually be dangerous. A review of 19 trials in which more than 19,000 participants took vitamin E for one reason or another (not just for dementia) found a slight but statistically meaningful increase in death rates in those who took doses of more than 150IU per day. So, given the low likelihood that vitamin E is of any use for preventing or treating dementia, and that high doses may slightly increase the chances of death, it doesn't actually have much good going for it.

However, some people just can't let go. Among the die-hard 'oxidationalists', the current thinking is that we just haven't tried the *right* antioxidant yet and so clinical trials are in preparation using new-generation antioxidant medications. I'm not holding my breath, but hopefully I'll be proved wrong! In the meantime, there is *no* good clinical evidence for taking vitamin C, vitamin E, selegiline, or any other antioxidant preparation for the *prevention of dementia.* On the other hand, a healthy range of food high in vitamin C and other natural antioxidants—such as capsicum, chillies, potatoes and citrus fruits—is important for good general health and should not be overlooked.

Ginkgo, bingo!

It seems that more people on the street have heard of the curative powers of the Chinese herb *ginkgo biloba* than just about any other dementia treatment, whether pharmaceutical or otherwise! Its repertoire is impressive, with claimed benefits for everything from erectile dysfunction to multiple sclerosis. Before we examine this intriguing plant extract in some detail in relation to dementia, here is the bottom line: ginkgo *may* have a role in the *treatment* of established dementia, but there is no good evidence to support using it to *prevent* dementia in the first place. It should also be stressed that even though ginkgo is a herbal preparation, and therefore thought of as 'complementary' or 'alternative', it does have side effects and can produce undesirable interactions when combined with conventional medications. Therefore, if you are going to trial ginkgo, make sure to inform your medical doctor.

Pharmacological studies suggest that ginkgo may have a number of effects on the human brain. First, it increases cerebral blood flow; this is interesting, since decreased blood flow at the capillary level may, as we considered in the previous chapter, be an important factor in both Vascular and Alzheimer's Dementia.

There is also evidence that ginkgo reduces the amount of swelling in the brain after minute trauma, that it may inhibit the formation of blood clots, and that it has antioxidant properties. And, of course, ginkgo (like most things, it seems) protects brain cells from the toxic effects of amyloid, at least in the petri dish.

The relative importance of these mechanisms with respect to why ginkgo appears to work as a treatment is simply not known. But it does seem to be effective. At least three clinical trials involving individuals already with mild to moderate dementia have shown significant therapeutic effects.

Most recently, one small but nevertheless sound clinical trial found that the therapeutic effect of taking EGb 761 (the active ingredient in *ginkgo biloba*) was basically the same as taking the current most effective medication.[2] Seventy-six individuals with mild to moderate AD dementia were randomly allocated to either 160 milligrams of daily ginkgo extract, or donepezil (one of a number of new-generation cholinesterase inhibitors which are licensed for treating AD dementia), or a placebo. Both the patients and researchers were unaware as to who was taking what, and so no subtle biases could cloud the results. Some six months later the researchers tested to see what changes had occurred on three simple measures of cognition and function. On one measure there were no differences; this was hardly surprising, as even the most effective current medications (such as donepezil) only work on about 30 per cent of people with AD dementia, and even then the effects seldom last beyond six months. On the other two measures, the placebo group declined more than both the ginkgo and donepezil groups; that is, both were equally effective, and both by modest amounts.

It seems ironic that ginkgo, one of the oldest plants known to humankind, may be just as effective for the treatment of AD dementia as the latest and greatest (and very expensive) medications. This, it should be emphasised, needs further corroboration by large, multinational clinical trials that are now under way. What I find most amazing about this humble herb is that, while its effectiveness appears to be no better or worse than current first-line medications (i.e., not that great), its side-effect profile does seem much better for patients.

Cholinesterase inhibitors are the class of medications—of which donepezil is one of many—that clinicians mainly use to treat AD dementia. As mentioned, their effectiveness is modest, but when they *do* work it can buy the individual and family some precious time. One of their main problems, however, is a high rate of unpleasant side effects. In clinical trials, these have occurred in anywhere between 10 and 30 per cent of individuals, and can include gastrointestinal problems, headache, sexual dysfunction and dry mouth, among other effects. In the trial mentioned above, for example, adverse events were reported in 16 per cent of the individuals on donepezil. Amazingly, no patient on ginkgo experienced any unpleasant event.

If the major trials replicate the same result as smaller trials and find ginkgo to be just as effective as the leading medicines, but with a fraction of the side effects and cost, then it doesn't take a brain scientist to work out what will happen! Perhaps it's not surprising that the Germans have been using ginkgo for the treatment of dementia for many years.

But on the question of using ginkgo for the *prevention* of *dementia*, there is very little data to go on, and the most recently reported trial has been quite negative. Dr Hiroko Dodge and colleagues from Oregon, in the United States, split 118 initially dementia-free individuals aged over 85 years into either a high-dose ginkgo regime (240 milligrams daily) or a placebo pill, and kept track of them for three years.[3] At the end of the study, 21 individuals had developed dementia, and importantly there were no significant differences in dementia rates between the groups. On a disturbing note, seven individuals taking ginkgo had suffered a stroke for the first time, while *none* of the placebo group did. It can be speculated that the increased blood flow promoted by ginkgo may come at the cost of an increased propensity to bleed.

Unfortunately, the numbers are so low that no firm conclusions can be made. As Dr Dodge commented in a press release:

These results need to be clarified with larger studies, but the findings are interesting because ginkgo biloba is already widely used, readily available, and relatively inexpensive … Further studies are needed to determine whether ginkgo biloba has any benefits in preventing cognitive decline and whether it is safe.[4]

For the moment there is no evidence that taking *ginkgo biloba* has any place in the prevention of dementia, and whether it is safe in otherwise well older individuals is not fully clear.

Can eating fish each day keep dementia at bay?

I must admit to being vegaquarian. I love seafood and come from a seafood-loving family. (My dad is a maestro with barbecued seafood, hailing from Valparaiso, the seafood capital of Chile.) I also like to keep fit, drink moderately, have never smoked, don't have high blood pressure, and so on. I have provided this information to illustrate an important point: that people's lifestyles and habits never occur in isolation. Therefore, one needs to put into perspective recent findings that individuals who eat oily fish such as salmon, tuna, sardines and cod more than twice a week are about half as likely to develop Alzheimer's Dementia as those who rarely eat oily fish. These results have been replicated in a handful of large epidemiological studies that track individuals initially without dementia for a number of years, and then try to isolate those factors that predict who will end up developing the condition.

Epidemiological research of this type is vastly important, but when associations like these are found, we need three additional streams of information *before we can conclude* that 'eating fish will reduce your risk for dementia'. First, we need to determine whether the linkage is independent of those other risk factors such as exercise, cardiovascular disease, education and so forth, which all tend to cluster together. Results from the epidemiological studies suggest that eating oily fish *is* associated with reduced dementia risk independent of these other risk factors. Good.

Next, there needs to be a plausible biological theory for how eating oily fish may alter dementia risk, with some experimental data to support it. The main argument here is that heavy chain omega-3 oils (such as docosahexaenoic acid, DHA) found in oily fish may have one of three possible effects: (1) an anti-amyloid effect, seen in reduced beta-amyloid formation in genetically engineered AD mice fed DHA; (2) a direct neuroprotective effect, because DHA forms a major part of the outer membrane of brain cells; and (3) an antioxidant or anti-inflammatory role.

But what about clinical trial evidence? Here is where the 'eat fatty fish' story gets a tad fishy. A clinical trial has been reported which used omega-3 supplements as a possible treatment for AD.[5] After 12 months of treatment there was no effect. Yet, *after the fact*, the authors noted a slight benefit in those patients at the lowest end of the clinical AD spectrum. This is known in scientific circles, rather appropriately, as 'fishing'. That is, when the main and secondary results don't turn out as expected, we tend to start looking for anything to hang a result on. Sometimes these *post hoc* findings can be pure gold, but most often they are just a product of the vicissitudes of that particular experiment. In any case, I would have thought these findings may be a clue that omega-3s are more effective as a *preventative* intervention, rather than a *therapeutic* one. Despite this, a trial is under way testing the efficacy of omega-3 supplementation for the treatment of full-blown AD dementia and is expected to report its findings in 2009. Until then, the link between eating oily fish and the prevention of Alzheimer's Dementia should only be considered as a potential one.

What we *do know*, however, is that omega-3 oils appear to be quite effective in combating heart disease. Epidemiological studies, biological experiments and clinical trials have all shown that omega-3 fatty acid supplements can reduce the incidence of cardio- and cerebrovascular events such as fatal heart attacks, non-fatal heart attacks and non-fatal strokes.[6] *For this reason alone, I therefore recommend including oily fish in one's regular diet.* Accordingly, I also suspect that a oily fish diet may be more effective for preventing Vascular Dementia, but this has yet to be tested in a formal clinical trial.

It should also be remembered that too much of a good thing, even fish, can be bad. Unfortunately, given the state of our seas and fisheries, some fish—including shark (flake), broadbill, marlin and swordfish—can contain relatively increased levels of heavy metals such as mercury. Food Standards Australia New Zealand suggests that for the general population these levels are still in the safe range for weekly consumption. However, for small children, and women who are pregnant, expecting to become pregnant or nursing small children, some restrictions apply. (For more details see the recommendations at the end of this chapter.) Intake of other sources of omega-3 fish oils—such as both fresh and canned tuna, salmon, trout, herring and sardines—is safe in Australia up to three times a week. Other sources of omega-3 oils include walnuts, flaxseed, canola oil and soya beans.

The 'French red wine paradox'

Similar conclusions related to eating oily fish apply to drinking red wine. As we shall see, this area has the additional complexities of how to define 'moderate drinking', and the issue of whether all forms of alcohol were created equally.

The origins of the 'French red wine paradox' stem from epidemiological observations in a study based partly around the Bordeaux area of France. In this study, a group of 3,777 non-demented elderly people still living at home underwent cognitive tests and completed an alcohol consumption questionnaire. At this baseline point in time, they were categorised as either non-drinkers, mild drinkers (1–2 drinks/day), moderate (3–4 drinks/day) or heavy (more than 4 drinks/day). As one would expect, wine was the main alcohol consumed among this cohort of older French citizens. The group has since been retested at regular intervals for more than ten years. Researchers found in 1997, at the three-year follow-up stage, that, compared to non-drinkers, those who drank moderately had about 20 per cent of the risk for developing dementia in general and 30 per cent of the risk for developing AD dementia specifically.

This fairly strong epidemiological association has been confirmed in one form or another in a number of studies conducted around the world. Some have even noted a correlation between the amount of wine consumed per capita and lower overall dementia rates for that country! Yet, despite these media-friendly findings, there is no overwhelming evidence to suggest that red wine, or wine in general, is more protective against dementia than any other form of alcohol. One large epidemiological study from Holland found no difference in dementia rates as a function of wine versus non-wine alcohol consumption, whereas similar studies from Italy and Denmark found more in favour of wine.

When we turn to a biological framework for the idea that moderate alcohol consumption may protect against dementia, all the usual suspects appear. Some believe there is an antioxidant effect, others that alcohol has anti-cardiovascular disease properties and yet others a mild anti-inflammatory mechanism. All have partial support in biological experiments. Yet, as we can imagine, no one has dared to run a clinical trial of moderate alcohol supplementation in teetotallers for the prevention of dementia! Such a trial is unlikely ever to happen, so we must conclude that there is only a *potential link* between moderate alcohol consumption and reduced dementia risk.

When it comes to advice on exactly what can be considered 'moderate', all sorts of problems arise. I remember asking an older patient how much he regularly drank, to which he replied: 'Just two glasses a night.' I asked, 'What do you drink?' and he replied, 'Scotch.' I then noticed a whole stack of empty Johnnie Walker bottles in a corner of his kitchen. 'What do you consider a glass?' I asked. He then pointed to something that better resembled a small vase!

Similar variation exists in what different nations call 'moderate drinking'. For example, in Australia, 10–30 grams of alcohol daily used to be thought of as 'moderate', but the National Health and Medical Research Council (NH&MRC) is currently undertaking a review that will probably lower this definition. Compare this with Italy, where 'moderate' alcohol consumption means up to 80 grams per day! And here we can see the source of another major confounding factor—the *way* we typically drink alcohol also varies greatly with culture and society. In Italy and many Mediterranean and Latin countries, a glass or two of wine with a meal is commonplace, and so explains the higher average number. In Australia, however, our drinking habits conform much more with the unhealthy binge-drinking pattern. The medical profession therefore tends to be more cautious about our alcohol recommendations because binge drinking, excessive regular drinking and alcohol dependence are all linked with ruinous health consequence for the heart, body and brain.

Given that the link between alcohol consumption and dementia is only a potential one, I therefore recommend that non-drinkers weigh the decision of whether to begin to drink (in moderation) very carefully indeed. Consider discussing this with your GP. For drinkers, a regular small dose—*Italian style*—is infinitely better than abstaining during the week and then getting your total weekly dose on Friday night. Avoid binge drinking all together. A glass or two of wine with dinner on most nights of the week seems to me a sensible option. This pattern of drinking may *potentially* lead to modest cardiovascular and cerebrovascular health benefits in the long term compared to not drinking at all, but this isn't likely ever to be confirmed definitively.

The sickly-sweet brain: Is there a link between diabetes and dementia?

Five out of seven major epidemiological studies from around the world have discovered an association between diabetes in late life and an increased risk for dementia.[7] What's more, two additional studies that assessed diabetes in mid-life found an increased risk for developing dementia up to 20 years later. While the link between type 2 diabetes and dementia is a relatively new one, it is exercising the minds of many in the field, because (a) we still don't know why there is an association, and (b) it holds out the promise that by better treating and preventing diabetes we might be able to prevent dementia.

The first and most likely clue to this riddle lies in the enigmatically titled **Metabolic X syndrome**. Also known as insulin resistance syndrome, the term refers to a cluster of abnormalities that occur increasingly with middle-age years: obesity, insulin resistance, cholesterol problems and hypertension. Sometimes just mild irregularities register in each area, which on their own would be of little concern, but together can contribute to an overall increased risk for cardiovascular disease. This collection of irregularities has become so common that it has also been somewhat unkindly referred to as MAS—*middle-age sprawl*. Yet, it is hardly a laughing matter given that some individuals develop such startling problems that both life and limb can be literally put in jeopardy.

The point about Metabolic X syndrome is that older individuals with diabetes are also almost certainly going to manifest problems in the other areas of obesity, hypertension and high cholesterol. Thus, it is very hard to determine whether the link between diabetes and dementia has more to do with the increased risk for cardiovascular disease *in general,* or is more specific to insulin resistance.

In fact, the link between diabetes and Vascular Dementia is generally more convincing than that for diabetes and Alzheimer's Dementia. The following results have been reported in population studies that were statistically adjusted for the presence or absence of other cardiac risk factors: all five of the studies that tested for a link with Vascular Dementia confirmed the association; only two of the five studies that specifically tested for a link with Alzheimer's Dementia found one. Having diabetes increases one's risk for stroke and cerebrovascular disease and therefore seems to put one at increased risk for Vascular Dementia.

Yet, the connection with Alzheimer's Dementia shouldn't be overlooked, for (as discussed in the previous chapter) the distinction between AD and VaD is becoming increasingly blurred. An increased blood glucose in the diabetic brain may prove noxious to brain cells generally, through a variety of mechanisms which together have been described as a form of 'accelerated ageing'. This includes increased oxidative stress and increased vulnerability to microvascular disease. More intense **microvascular disease**, which includes clogged capillaries, ischemia and microbleeds, could therefore also feed into the Alzheimer's amyloid pathway, as suggested in the previous chapter.

Another hypothesis is that the high level of insulin in the brains of individuals with diabetes may interfere with, or even destroy, the principal protein whose job it is to get rid of it: Insulin Degrading Enzyme (IDE). It is therefore hardly coincidental that IDE also happens to be one of the main enzymes responsible for breaking down the amyloid plaques that define AD. Individuals who die with AD dementia have significantly reduced levels of IDE in their hippocampus, the main memory area of the brain and the area most affected in AD. And, of course, transgenic rats engineered to express the human amyloid proteins show increased levels of pathology when put on a 'diabetic diet' and, conversely, improve both on memory tests and neuropathologically when treated with diabetic medication.

There are therefore reasonable grounds to speculate that some aspect of the diabetes process may also be driving dementia, either through vascular- or amyloid-related mechanisms. One clinical trial found improvement in AD dementia patients' mental abilities after starting a diabetic medication called *rosiglitazone*. There are now at least six clinical trials under way by drug companies to determine whether this commonly used medication can improve outcomes for Alzheimer's Dementia. The results of these trials are expected in the next couple of years. I am unaware of any similar trials planned in relation to Vascular Dementia.

Interestingly, the small clinical trials completed so far suggest an effect only in those patients who were negative for the APOE4 gene. As we shall see in the next chapter, APOE is a gene that regulates cholesterol metabolism in each and every brain cell. We will devote some time to trying to understand how this may work, because this just may be the clue that helps to link Alzheimer's Dementia not only with cholesterol, but also with diabetes, omega-3 fish oils, cardiovascular disease and even mental activity.

Lesson #2: *A balanced Mediterranean-style diet with increased fish and moderate alcohol almost certainly reduces your risk for cardiovascular disease. It also potentially reduces your risk for Vascular and Alzheimer's Dementia.*

Recommendation #2: *Adopt the Mediterranean lifestyle of including regular oily fish in your diet and, if a drinker, moderate regular alcohol.*

HOW DO I DO THIS?

- Try the *Healthy Brain Meal Plan* in the *In Focus* section of this chapter.
- Include *low-risk* oily fish in your meals two to three times a week. *Low-risk* oily fish includes tuna, salmon, sardines, herring and many others.
- High-risk fish includes perch (orange roughy), catfish, flake (shark) and billfish (swordfish, broadbill, marlin). High-risk fish should be limited to once per week, with no other fish that week.

- **Warning!** Small children, pregnant women, and those planning pregnancy or nursing children need to further limit *high-risk* oily fish. Individuals in this category can safely eat one serving of perch or catfish per week (with no other fish), or one serving of billfish or flake per *fortnight* (and no other fish).

- For more information about safe seafood guidelines, go to: <www.foodstandards.gov.au/newsroom/foodstandards news/foodstandardsnews49a2423.cfm#_mercury>

- Include other omega-3-rich sources in your diet, such as walnuts, canola oil, flaxseed and soya beans.

- If a non-drinker, only take up drinking alcohol for health reasons after discussing this with your GP.

- If a drinker, avoid binge drinking.

- If a drinker, regular modest amounts of alcohol are recommended. The current NH&MRC guidelines for low-risk alcohol consumption (published in 2001) are currently under review. Latest updates, and more specific information for individuals with special considerations are available at <www.alcohol.gov.au>. You can also ask your GP for more current information. At the time of going to print, recommendations were:
  - *For men:* no more than four standard drinks a day on average, and no more than six standard drinks on any given day. One or two alcohol-free days per week.

- *For women:* no more than two standard drinks a day on average, and no more than four standard drinks on any given day. One or two alcohol-free days per week.

Lesson #3: *There is a strong possibility that diabetes is linked to dementia.*

Recommendation #3: *Avoid diabetes in the first place.*

HOW DO I DO THIS?

- Ask your GP for a fasting blood sugar test.
- It's easy to remember! All those things that help in avoiding high blood pressure (see Chapter 3) also help in avoiding diabetes.
- Exercise is a particularly powerful way to decrease your long-term blood sugar, by increasing not only your active metabolism, but also your resting metabolism (see Chapter 3).
- Maintain a healthy diet, which means not taking in more energy than you expend. Complete a physical activity assessment to work out how many kilojoules you use in a week <www.caloriesperhour.com/index_burn.php>
- If you are eating more kilojoules than this, you need either to increase your exercise accordingly or reduce your energy intake. To calculate how much energy and

nutrients there are in a particular food portion, see <www.thecaloriecounter.com>

- A healthy diet also means eating the right mix of foods. A balanced diet is best. The federal Department of Health and Ageing has released the *Australian Guide to Healthy Eating*, which is available free of charge by entering the full guide's name into Google and following the links.
- To summarise, the above Guide recommends that we eat a wide range of foods across the food groups, and add more variety within the food groups as well. Proportionally, we should eat grains, breads and cereals the most, followed by vegetables, then dairy, fruits, meats and, finally, fats. Highly processed foods and sugary treats should be infrequent.
- At the same time, the federal government began its '2 & 5' campaign to encourage Australians to eat more veggies (five serves a day) and fruits (two serves a day). The campaign is a long-overdue response to the alarming increase in obesity in this country, and to the fact that very little advertising is commissioned to champion these foods. The website for this campaign has some interesting information, as well as easy recipes: <www.gofor2and5.com.au>
- For a weekly plan that is particularly high in good 'brain food', try the *Healthy Brain Meal Plan* in this chapter's *In Focus.*

WHAT IF I ALREADY HAVE DIABETES?

You need to keep doing all the healthy things mentioned above AND aim for optimal blood sugar control in consultation with your GP or specialist. To do so means *regular* health checks.

IN FOCUS   The Healthy Brain Meal Plan

The principles of eating for a *healthy brain* are simple:

1. Lots of vegetables, cereals and fruit, with a bias towards high-antioxidant choices.

2. Generous amounts of fish and seafood throughout the week.

3. Wine with dinner every other night and plenty of water throughout the day.

4. High calcium through low-fat dairy products.

5. Low levels of fat, preferring mono-unsaturated varieties over saturated fats.

Any meal plan, however, will become unhealthy if the amount of energy taken in isn't counter-balanced by enough exercise to use it up; that's how we become overweight, which by itself has been linked to dementia. I have therefore included a range of daily plans, from a low to a moderate caloric intake. At the end of the plan is a table showing how much exercise would be needed to burn off this week's intake of delicious and nutritious food.

This meal plan is, of course, just an example. It is mainly intended to inspire. Mix it up, add your own ideas, make double servings that will last for two days, and so on. Have fun creating your own eating plan for a healthy brain.

SAMPLE MENUS

Monday
Breakfast
- 1 tub low-fat yoghurt
- 1 piece of fruit of your choice
- 1 slice wholegrain toast with thin spread of butter
- 1 cup of tea or coffee with calcium-enriched low-fat milk

Calories: 326

Water!

Lunch
Trout nicoise salad
Combine 100g smoked trout pieces (available from the supermarket as fillets), 1 teaspoon capers, 1 boiled egg, salad leaves, boiled green beans, cherry tomatoes, 5 olives and a sliced small potato. Dressing: 1 teaspoon olive oil, juice of ½ lemon, 1 teaspoon seeded mustard. Salt and pepper to taste. Nice with a small French baguette.

Calories: 650

Snack
Handful of mixed nuts
Calories: 270

Water!

Dinner
Chana masala (Classic Indian chickpea curry)
In mono-unsaturated canola oil, briefly sear the spices:
1 teaspoon curry powder (more to taste), tumeric and a small
quantity of fennel seeds. Add in 3 cloves crushed garlic, 1 red
chilli, 1 well-chopped small onion and half a chopped red
capsicum. When soft, add 1 can of drained chickpeas (keep the
liquid) with a tablespoon of butter and stir vigorously on high
heat. When the spices have coated all the chickpeas, add liquid
from chickpeas and 1 cup of water so that ingredients are just
covered. Bring down heat to simmer without a lid to reduce
and thicken curry sauce. Make boiled basmati rice at the same
time. Serve curry and rice with lots of fresh coriander over the
top. Finely chopped tomato, onion and Lebanese cucumber
salad with lemon juice dressing is a perfect accompaniment.
Serves 3–4.
Calories: 423 per serve

Water!
Daily total: 1,669 calories

Tuesday

Breakfast

1 cup ricotta cheese mixed with passionfruit (in summer) or
cinnamon, honey and almonds (in winter)
1 cup of tea or coffee with calcium-enriched low-fat milk
Calories: 491

Water!

Lunch

Fetta and beetroot salad

Halve 5 tinned baby beets. Gently boil 1 cup green peas and
add 1 cup baby spinach leaves to the water to wilt them when
the peas are almost cooked. Salad is composed of 5 cubes of
fetta cheese, the beetroot, 1 sliced Spanish onion, baby spinach
and green peas. Dressing: 1 teaspoon olive oil, juice of
1 orange, 1 teaspoon balsamic vinegar and salt/pepper to taste.
Calories: 443

Snack

Banana
Calories: 121

Water!

Dinner

Salmon & snow pea stir-fry

In a wok on high heat, briefly fry 2 cloves crushed garlic, green
chilli and 1 chopped onion, salt and pepper, using mono-
unsaturated canola oil. Add small portions of high-grade
salmon steak (500g) and stir-fry until half-done. Remove fish

and add carrot slices, red capsicum slivers and cashews. When soft, add de-veined snow peas and then bean spouts—toss. Re-introduce fish for final stir-fry and add teriyaki sauce. Serve instantly with plain boiled rice. Serves 2.
Calories: 881 per serve

Water!
Daily total: 1,936 calories

Wednesday
Breakfast
Quick-cook oats made with milk, honey and fresh chopped peaches (in summer) or canned plums (in winter)
1 cup of tea or coffee with calcium-enriched low-fat milk
Calories: 261

Water!

Lunch
Salad sandwich plus grapes
Calories: 323

Snack
Handful of dried fruits and nuts
Calories: 254

Water!

Dinner
Lamb backstrap with parmesan potato and kumera bake
Lamb backstrap: Coat frypan with 1 teaspoon of olive oil. Add 1 finely chopped garlic clove and the leaves from 2 sprigs of

rosemary. Sear both sides of a 200g trim lamb backstrap and then reduce the heat to allow lamb to cook through. Allow lamb to sit for 5 minutes prior to serving.

Parmesan potato and kumera bake: Boil 2 medium potatoes and 1 medium kumera. Thinly slice the potato, kumera and 1 Spanish onion and layer into a small baking pan lined with lightly oiled baking paper. Place 50g shaved parmesan cheese and sprigs of thyme and crushed sage leaves between the layers. Season well with pepper and 1 teaspoon crushed nutmeg. Pour over 1 lightly beaten egg. Bake until golden brown. Serves 1.
Calories: 1,212

Water!
Daily total: 2,050 calories

Thursday

Breakfast
2 pieces of fruit of your choice
2 slices wholegrain toast with olive oil spread
1 cup of tea or coffee with calcium-enriched low-fat milk
Calories: 320

Water!

Lunch
Leftover parmesan potato and kumera bake with fresh garden salad dressed with juice of half a lemon and pepper.
Calories: 298

Snack: Small portion of cheese and crackers
Calories: 547

Water!

Dinner
Whole baked snapper

This dish is so easy and quite versatile. The secret is to find a quality fishmonger that sells beautiful fresh fish. The fish shop should smell sweet and of-the-sea, rather than 'fishy'. Ask for a whole medium-sized snapper, cleaned out, and their advice on how long it should take to cook in foil.

Arrange an extra-long piece of aluminium foil in an oven dish so that, once you have finished preparing the fish, it is easy to seal it in an air-tight envelope.

Cover both sides of the fish with plenty of salt and pepper.

For a Mediterranean-style fish, place the fish on a bed of fresh fennel strips so that the fish steam-cooks, rather than boils. Stuff the belly with fresh pieces of fennel, mint, Spanish onion rings and a couple of lime wedges. You can make some thick cuts into the exposed flank and insert more fennel or garlic. Drizzle a generous amount of olive oil over the top. Importantly, add 4 tablespoons of water. Close the envelope carefully and place into the medium/hot oven for the required time. When the time is up, carefully open the envelope and check that the meat in the inner side of the belly is opaque-white (cooked), rather than semi-translucent (undercooked). If underdone, put back in the oven but don't overcook it!

For a Chinese-style fish, place on a bed of bok choy and stuff with shallots, fresh ginger, bamboo shoots, and sliced oyster and Swiss brown mushrooms. Instead of water, use soy sauce. Serves 2–3.

Serve either combination with plain boiled rice and steamed veggies.

Strawberries and frozen yoghurt after dinner.

Calories: 842

Water!
Daily total: 2,007 calories

Friday
Breakfast
1-egg omelette with fresh herbs of your choice, 3 sliced button
or Swiss brown mushrooms and 10g parmesan cheese
1 piece of wholegrain toast
1 cup of tea or coffee with calcium-enriched low-fat milk.
Calories: 290

Water!

Lunch
Rye bread avocado sandwich plus fresh fruit (peach in
summer, pear in winter)
Calories: 390

Snack
Tub of yoghurt
Calories: 143

Water!

Dinner
Linguini vongole
No one wants to cook a complicated meal on Friday night.
This dish is 100 per cent mafia and deliciously easy! Bring a
large quantity of salted water to the boil and add 300g good
quality linguini—cook til al dente. At the same time, sauté in a
large frypan 3 cloves of crushed garlic together with a finely
chopped onion and a red capsicum, using a tablespoon of
butter, olive oil, salt, pepper and a pinch of oregano. When
soft, add 300g fresh vongole (clams) and turn up heat. Within
5 minutes, they will start to open. Add ⅓ glass of white wine

and reduce for 2 minutes. Done. Add drained pasta to saucepan, mix and serve. Accompany with insalata caprese made with ripe tomatoes, baby bocconcini, basil leaves and olive oil, and a warm dinner bread roll. *Manja bene!*
Serves 2.
Wine: 1–2 glasses Sauvignon Blanc
Calories: 996 per person

Water!
Daily total: 1,819 calories

Saturday
Breakfast
1 bagel topped with 2 tablespoons low-fat cream cheese, 2 slices smoked salmon, diced Spanish onion, capers and a squeeze of lemon
1 cup of tea or coffee with calcium-enriched low-fat milk
Calories: 453

Water!

Lunch
Chilean corn and basil mash
Friends and family will love this classic and delicious summer treat from South America.
You will need 12 fresh whole corn ears, half a bunch of basil, 1 large onion, olive oil, salt and pepper. Peel, remove corn silk and wash corn. Carefully strip kernels from corn with a knife. Gradually transfer to a blender and puree with basil leaves. Consistency should remain coarse. Transfer puree to large saucepan and *slowly* bring to simmer, stirring *often* (very important). In a frypan sauté finely chopped onion, adding

salt and pepper and optional green chillies. Add fried onion to simmering puree and stir frequently for 30 minutes. If puree becomes too thick, add small quantity of milk. (Soya milk is fine.) Adjust seasoning to taste. Serve in a rustic ceramic bowl and garnish with basil leaf. Serve with side salad of tomato, oil and chopped coriander, and warm ciabata bread. (Note: When simmering, use a lid or risk a mess!) Serves 4.

Wine: 1–2 glasses Cabernet Sauvignon
Calories: 914 per person

Snack
Olives, gherkins, dip and wholemeal pita bread
Calories: 222

Water!

Dinner
Roast vegetable soup
A light supper is in order after such a filling and nutritious lunch. This soup is the ultimate comfort food. Bake sweet potato, whole garlic cloves (in skin) and red capsicum in oven until caramelized. Peel black crust off capsicums and squeeze out garlic paste. Chop roughly and put in blender or food processor until smooth. In a saucepan with olive oil, fry more chopped garlic, shallots and half a thinly diced celery stick, with salt and pepper. When soft, add in vegetable puree and a small amount of water. Simmer for a few minutes. Serve with warm crusty bread and extra cracked pepper.
Calories: 570

Water!
Daily total: 2,159 calories

Sunday
Breakfast
2 wholemeal pancakes with dried cranberries or sultanas.
Serve with sliced banana
1 cup of tea or coffee with calcium-enriched low-fat milk
Calories: 335

Water!

Lunch
Tuna & king prawn shish
Ready in 15 minutes ... perfect on the barbecue or under the grill. Start with two excellent sashimi-grade tuna steaks and 750g large green king prawns. (Peel, leaving tails on, and de-vein.) Put shish-sticks in water for an hour beforehand. Arrange shish in the following order: red capsicum, tuna, large caperberry, prawn, capsicum, tuna, caperberry, etc. Roll in finely chopped garlic and sprinkle with lemon rind. Add salt and pepper to taste. Cook 3–4 minutes on high heat per side. Serve with mashed potato and cos lettuce salad dressed with lemon and olive oil. Serves 4.
Wine: 1–2 glasses Semillon/Sauvignon Blanc blend
Calories: 1,053 per person

Snack
Home-blended apple, ginger and carrot juice
Calories: 190

Water!

Dinner
Moroccan chicken on couscous pilaf
Lightly coat a frypan with 1 teaspoon olive oil. Add 1 garlic
clove, 1 small red chilli, 1 teaspoon paprika and 1 teaspoon
cumin seeds to oil. Lightly fry 1 chicken breast in the seasoned
oil, adding salt and pepper to taste.
Couscous: Boil 1 cup vegetable stock, then pour over 1 cup
couscous and allow to stand for 5 minutes. Dice 1 tomato,
1 avocado, 1 Spanish onion and ½ cup coriander, and mix
through the couscous. Top with the chicken breast.
Calories: 961

Water!
Daily total: 2,539 calories

HOW MANY CALORIES DO YOU NEED?

As mentioned earlier in this chapter, the best way to determine
your daily caloric needs is to use one of the suggested online
calculators. Many factors are important, including your age, sex,
height and weight—and, of course, your activity pattern. Below
is a table comparing the estimated daily caloric needs for males
versus females of the same Body-to-Mass Index, at different
ages and different activity patterns.

Note how, as we get older, we need somewhat fewer calories
per day, but this can be more than offset by an active lifestyle
pattern.

This *Healthy Brain Meal Plan* has a weekly total of 14,179 calories, which translates to an average daily intake of about 2,024 calories.

Using the table below, compare this to how many calories you may be currently burning per day.

	AGE	SEDENTARY	ACTIVE
MALES			
175cm, 75kg	30	2,100 calories	2,550 calories
BMI=24.5	60	1,900 calories	2,250 calories
FEMALES			
165cm, 67kg	30	1,750 calories	2,100 calories
BMI=24.6	60	1,600 calories	1,900 calories

CHAPTER 5

What's the story with cholesterol?

Most of us would be aware that keeping our cholesterol under control is important for maintaining good physical health. Furthermore, we may also be familiar with the distinction between 'good' cholesterol and 'bad' cholesterol. Yet, even the medically literate may be surprised to learn that the link between cholesterol, brain function and dementia is emerging as a potential clue in the Alzheimer puzzle.

How does the body manage cholesterol levels?

The way our bodies handle cholesterol is complex, but it is worthwhile trying to come to grips with how it enters our system, how it is internally metabolised, and then how we get rid of it. Let's start with the big picture. Cholesterol enters our bodies via our diet. Animal fats and eggs are the sole natural sources of cholesterol. It is absorbed through our gut and travels via the blood supply to the liver. In fact, after a heavy meal our blood can turn milky from all the absorbed fat and cholesterol floating around as mini fatty droplets! The liver takes up these floating cholesterol complexes and then coordinates two parallel metabolic processes. The first completes what is called the *exogenous pathway*, which closes the loop, so to speak. Cholesterol and bile acids are pumped out of the liver and stored in the gall bladder; they then re-enter the gut, where they help in digestion and are re-absorbed once again, or they are eliminated when we go to the bathroom. Hence, any blockage to the 'biliary system', such as a gall bladder stone, will lead to an increase in blood plasma cholesterol, among other effects.

The second process has been termed the *endogenous pathway*, for it describes how the liver and body break down and resynthesise cholesterol outside of the gut. Our liver routinely re-forms cholesterol as a very low-density cholesterol (VLDL), which is carried through the blood and converted via enzymes in the capillaries to **low-density cholesterol** (LDL). LDL receptors in the liver mean that the liver can function like a thermostat for maintaining LDL levels evenly: high LDL leads to a decrease in VLDL production, and vice versa. LDL is taken up by every cell in the body, as it forms a key component of the cell membrane.

Even *within* the cell after it has taken up LDL, there is a form of 'negative feedback' control. As more LDL is taken up, fewer receptors are produced on the cell surface and so restrict how much LDL can enter. LDL entry also inhibits the re-formation of cholesterol within the cell by reducing a key cellular enzyme called *HMG-CoA reductase*. Statins, one of the most commercially successful drugs of all time, reduce blood plasma cholesterol with a minimum of fuss by suppressing the activity of this key enzyme.

Cholesterol leaves our cells in the form of **high-density lipoproteins** (HDLs), for which there are also a special class of receptors in the liver. They can be re-absorbed from the blood, and then reconverted to another form and reused, or are broken down and eliminated via the exogenous system. These somewhat complex processes are summarised in Figure 3.

It is abundantly clear, therefore, that the human body has evolved a highly sophisticated system for keeping our cholesterol levels on an even keel. The liver acts as a conductor of sorts, managing how much comes in and out, and how much to convert from one form to another. Furthermore, the body takes a multilevel approach, for every cell is also equipped with 'negative feedback' mechanisms to ensure that they don't absorb too much cholesterol.

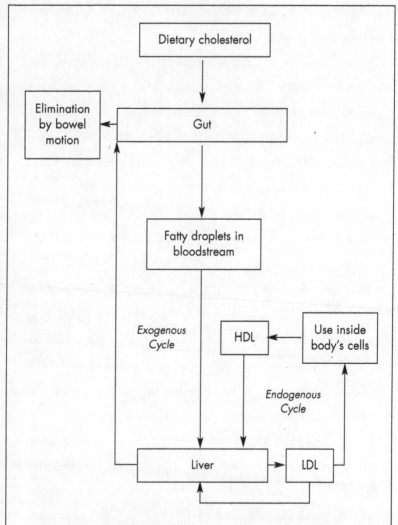

Figure 3 A very simple schematic of the way cholesterol is handled by the human body. Note that the exogenous system essentially cycles cholesterol through the gut, while in the endogenous system cholesterol is formed and re-formed via the liver.

What happens when we consume too much dietary cholesterol?

In general, the body's finely tuned system does a marvellous job. The fundamental problem for us in modern society is that evolution hasn't been able to keep up with our lifestyle and diet trends. We now consume so much animal fat and cholesterol-rich foods that our liver and cells just can't cope. This excess in dietary cholesterol means that cells and blood become saturated in LDL cholesterol. A particularly nasty chain of events then begins in our arteries and blood vessels, with cholesterol-laden cells depositing along their inner walls, and the development of plaques and inflammation. Our arteries begin to narrow and stiffen, resulting in reduced blood flow and responsiveness, which in the heart's main vessels leads to angina. Sometimes these plaques become unstable and break off, or the vessel simply clogs up completely, producing a heart attack or stroke.

Fortunately for us, modern medical science understands this complex biology. We can now manage the build-up of noxious cholesterol in our blood vessels in a relatively safe and convenient manner, by both pharmacological and non-pharmacological means. This, in turn, has contributed to the steady improvement in the incidence of atherosclerosis, heart attack, unstable angina and deaths related to cardiovascular disease in developed countries over the last 20 years. Our life expectancy has accordingly risen over the same period. But the unforeseen consequence of this medical success story is that for every five years gained beyond 65 years of age, our chances of getting dementia more than doubles. Yet, in an equally unforeseen development, the same cholesterol metabolism pathway that has been implicated in our increased longevity may also be implicated in Alzheimer's Disease.

Is there a link between cholesterol and brain function?

The fatty brain

Surprisingly, the brain is our most cholesterol-rich organ. Human brain cells have evolved in a very specific way to handle cholesterol and for a specific purpose. Rather than rely on dietary cholesterol or the cholesterol made and transformed in the liver, the brain produces its own through the work of an under-appreciated class of brain cells called **astrocytes**. Cholesterol produced in the astrocytes is moved into neurons via one of an important class of transporter molecules called **apolipoprotein E** (APOE). Our neurons internalise the APOE complex, which is then processed by the tiny organelles within the brain cell. This brain-cell-processed cholesterol is then inserted into the cell's membrane as **cholesterol lipid rafts**—small patches within the brain cell's outer membrane where the cholesterol is concentrated and 'floats' like a platform. Figure 4 depicts some of this sequence in a simplistic diagram.

There is now a whole sub-branch of neurobiology detailing how dozens of brain membrane receptors and enzymes rely *critically* on the proper density and conformation of these lipid rafts. Amazingly, the production of beta-amyloid, the hypothesised key pathological agent for Alzheimer's Disease in classical thinking, also depends on the activity of these cholesterol lipid rafts.

To our best knowledge, in order for beta-amyloid to be produced outside of the cell, at least three critical events need to occur. First, the amyloid precursor protein (APP) (the long protein that spans both the inside and outside of the brain cell) needs to be chopped internally by an enzyme called alpha-secretase. (Figure 4 may be helpful here, as the explanation gets somewhat jargon-heavy.) Alpha-secretase doesn't appear to be in direct contact with cholesterol lipid rafts. Next, beta-secretase (BACE) and then **gamma-secretase** chop APP to release beta-amyloid into the extracellular space. Both these enzymes *are* in direct contact with cholesterol lipid rafts.

Biological studies have shown that reducing cellular cholesterol inhibits BACE activity and thereby reduces extracellular beta-amyloid.[1] One method of reducing cellular cholesterol is by treating the cells with minute dosages of statins, those same medicines commonly used to lower cholesterol for

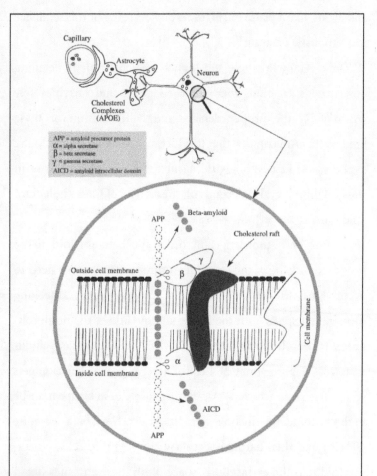

Figure 4 The top figure shows the 'holy trinity' of the brain: neuron, astrocyte and capillary. Cholesterol is synthesised in the astrocyte and is then transported into the neuron as APOE cholesterol complexes. The lower part of the figure zooms into the neuron's outer cell membrane, showing how the cholesterol raft is an integral part, helping the function of alpha-, beta- and gamma-secretases, which sequentially chop up amyloid precursor protein (APP) and thereby release beta-amyloid into the extracellular space.

heart disease. Studies in genetically modified mice which over-express beta-amyloid have shown that treatment with statins lowers their beta-amyloid production and development of AD pathology. Humans treated with statins also appear to reduce the amount of beta-amyloid production as detected in the cerebrospinal fluid (CSF) after a lumbar puncture.

Clinical trials

As you may have come to expect, the happy pattern seen in the lab, in animal research and even in some human experimental work hasn't, unfortunately, translated to positive results when tested in clinical trials. Clinicians had grounds to anticipate a positive effect, because epidemiological studies had revealed a link between high cholesterol levels in mid-life and increased chances of AD dementia in late life; furthermore, those already being treated with a statin seemed to have a reduced risk for the development of dementia in long-term follow-up studies.

Results of the PROSPER (Prospective study of pravastatin in the elderly at risk) study, a randomised clinical trial, were therefore highly anticipated, and deeply disappointing. Almost 6,000 individuals with high cholesterol to start with and risk for cardiovascular disease were randomly allocated to either a statin or placebo pill. Follow-up three years later found no difference in the rates of dementia in both groups, completely against expectations. Drug companies and some researchers have criticised the study for not trialling the 'right' statin, and have highlighted other methodological issues. Nine randomised control trials are currently under way to test further the effects of these medicines for dementia.

To add to the confusion, more recent work has begun to question the original studies linking blood cholesterol levels and dementia.[2] For example, post-mortem studies show that AD patients actually have *less* cholesterol in the membrane of their brain cells than their healthy counterparts, and so further reduction through use of statins may actually do more harm than good. One transgenic AD mouse study, for example, found *increased* beta-amyloid plaque formation, rather than decreased formation as reported in a prior study. Detailed experimental studies have also emphasised the 'disconnect' that can occur between peripheral cholesterol (what our GP measures via a blood sample) and brain cholesterol—showing that it is possible to have *heightened* blood cholesterol but *lowered* brain cholesterol. Some follow-up epidemiological studies have also now failed to find a link between statin usage and new onset of dementia, bringing into question the earlier data that suggested such a relationship.

An even more troubling interpretation is, of course, that the classical beta-amyloid hypothesis just isn't right. If experimental studies can show that statin treatment reduces CSF amyloid by up to a massive 40 per cent, yet a large multinational clinical trial has shown no effect on dementia rates, then something is clearly amiss. As mentioned elsewhere in this book, by focusing on beta-amyloid rather than synaptic function, there has been an assumption that elimination of beta-amyloid should automatically lead to protection against dementia. However, the relationship between synaptic function, cholesterol, beta-amyloid and dementia is more subtle and dynamic than previously supposed.

If, for example; we turn off beta-amyloid production by switching off gamma-secretase, the neuron dies, at least *in vitro*. In what some scientists have figuratively likened to awakening from a bad dream, the proper physiological role of beta-amyloid is only now beginning to be appreciated. Some groups have shown that beta-amyloid can serve an antioxidant role, by counteracting the toxic effects of unstable metals floating within and around the cell. Others have noted that beta-amyloid can provide a negative feedback role in relation to synaptic firing; when firing rates become so high that the cell risks build-up of toxic by-products, beta-amyloid signals the cell to slow down.

Findings such as these are starting to challenge the dogmatic view that beta-amyloid is bad and needs to be eliminated. These results also provoke questions about why, then, do we see so much beta-amyloid in AD? In fact, we *define* AD by the presence of beta-amyloid in the brain (among other pathological changes), which has in my view seduced scientists into assuming that it must have a causal role in the memory and functional problems of dementia. A growing band of scientists are now forming the view that the increased beta-amyloid witnessed in AD may, alternatively, be a sign of the brain's proper adaptation and compensation to an as-yet-unidentified problem further 'upstream'.

Similarly, an essential degree of cholesterol content is required in the brain cell's membrane for proper synaptic function. The synapse—that critical juncture by which neurons communicate with each other—is, relatively speaking, crammed full of both APP and cholesterol lipid rafts. Cholesterol is particularly enriched at the synaptic membrane and its many sub-components. The simple addition of cholesterol to neurons in the lab greatly increases the number of synapses as well as the formation of specialised sub-units that carry the **neurotransmitter** chemicals to the synaptic junction, thereby allowing transmission of information from one brain cell to another.

Genetics, cholesterol and dementia

A recent study has found that gamma-secretase enzyme activity may participate in *both* the production of beta-amyloid *and* the entry of cholesterol into the brain cell via the APOE transporter molecule. This is therefore the first piece of evidence—at least, in mice—to establish a molecular link between the classical beta-amyloid processing pathway and cholesterol metabolism. On the other hand, gamma-secretase function also relies on the proper concentration and activity of the surrounding cholesterol lipid rafts. Hence, it appears that amyloid and cholesterol metabolism are interdependent in a biological process of exceeding complexity.

What moves all this complex biology beyond the merely academic is that, of the millions of genes screened for an association with dementia, it is only APOE that has an established connection. So, if you have a first-degree relative with dementia, then your chances of also getting dementia are greater than otherwise. To what extent one's risk is increased is complicated, and seems to depend on both the age of dementia onset in your relative and your own current age. For example, if your first-degree relative developed AD dementia early on (close to 60 years of age), and you are now aged 60 yourself, then your risk for dementia in the next ten years is ten times higher than for those individuals with first-degree relatives who developed dementia in their eighties. On the other hand, if the same person was to reach their late seventies without developing dementia, there is no increased risk for dementia in the next ten years due to the fact of having a relative with dementia that began in their early sixties. Complicated, right? In any case, as far as we can tell, this complex hereditary association is associated with what type of APOE gene you carry in your DNA.

The **APOE gene** is found on chromosome 19 and codes for one of three variants—APOE2, APOE3 or APOE4. Since we get a copy from each parent, we can therefore carry one of six APOE 'signatures': 2/2, 2/3, 3/3, 3/4, 2/4 or 4/4. The difference in the final APOE protein produced by our brain cells as a result of our genetic inheritance is truly minute. Two hundred and ninety-nine amino acids make up the APOE protein, and the difference between a 2/2 and a 4/4 gene carrier is as little as four miserly amino acids. Yet, these four amino acids make a significant impact. For every '4' in one's APOE gene code, the average age of dementia onset is lowered by as much as eight years. Individuals with one APOE4 gene are three times more likely to develop dementia in their lifetime; those with two APOE4s, have eight times more risk.

How and why the APOE4 strain confers the increased dementia risk is currently unknown. It has been speculated that this strain may be more 'amyloidgenic'—that is, it may disrupt proper cholesterol levels within the cell membrane and lead to increased production of beta-amyloid—or perhaps may be directly neurotoxic itself. Unfortunately, for the moment all this is pure supposition.

SHOULD I GET MY APOE4 STATUS CHECKED?

Understandably, the discovery of genetic risk factors for a disease can be unsettling. While the APOE4 linkage to dementia has been known for some time, it is not common knowledge. There are a number of reasons for this.

First, as a general principle, the medical profession doesn't advocate testing for genetic risk factors unless there is something one can do about it. Since, at the moment, there is no cast-iron proven strategy for the prevention of dementia—regardless of APOE4 status—it would seem altogether nihilistic to have this information and not have a strategy for positive action.

Second, there is no guarantee, even if you carry the 4/4 'double dose', that you will necessarily develop dementia. Yes, your chances are higher than for the rest of the population, but it's not a foregone conclusion.

Third, should you get a result (for example) in your middle-age years, 20–30 years before dementia becomes a realistic risk, new interventions and treatments for dementia may well be developed in the interim.

Hence, it seems that the only outcome of an APOE4 result *now* is worry. There is no upside. The balance of the clinical equation is all negative. Indeed, if you wished to proceed with this test, you would need to pay for it yourself.

I will certainly *not* be getting an APOE4 test until there is a definite preventative treatment for this genetic risk factor. In the meantime, we're all in the same boat. What we have are a number of potential and possible preventative strategies, which, cumulatively, will hopefully reduce our chances of getting dementia. Hence, the motivation for this book!

Lesson #3: *Keeping HDL cholesterol up and LDL cholesterol down almost certainly reduces your risk for cardiovascular disease. There is no good evidence it reduces your risk for AD dementia.*

Recommendation #3: *Keep your cholesterol healthy.*

HOW DO I DO THIS?

- Get your cholesterol checked by your GP.
- If high, review your diet and physical activity levels. (See the recommendations at the end of Chapter 3.)
- Medical options: Discuss with your GP the pros and cons of starting statin treatment after trying dietary and lifestyle changes.

IN FOCUS Dementia doesn't always strike late

*Alzheimer's Dementia is predominately a disease of later life, but not always. In fact, **younger onset dementia** presents unique challenges to the patient, their family, the health system, and how society responds to their illness. In this special section, Dr Adrienne Withall, a psychologist who has specialised in research about young-onset dementia, discusses this condition, and explains what is currently known about its origins and what we can do about.*

'Younger onset dementia' refers to changes in a person's memory, judgment or behaviour that occur prior to the age of 65. Dementia earlier on in life can be incredibly disruptive to the family unit. People may have young spouses and children still living at home, and be at the peak of their careers with significant financial commitments. Premature retirement and loss of their driving licence can be extremely demoralising for the affected individual, and their distress can radiate throughout the family. In some instances, an older parent may have to reprise their former role and take on the care of their son or daughter with dementia, as well as their grandchildren.

Dementia in younger persons is more common than you might think. The illness affects about one in every 2,000 persons aged 30 to 44 years and one in every 1,000 persons aged 45 to 64. Dementia can also affect children, teens and young adults, although this is quite rare. Whereas Alzheimer's Disease is the main cause of dementia in people over 65, it accounts for only one-third of cases in younger people. Other causes of dementia in younger persons include frontotemporal dementia (which often starts as behavioural changes such as aggression, personality changes, emotional withdrawal and/or language problems), Lewy body dementia, and dementia associated with other illnesses—for example, Parkinson's disease, Huntington's disease or multiple sclerosis.

Also of note is that there are a number of preventable causes of dementia in this younger age group. These include Vascular Dementia, alcohol-related dementia, dementia due to head injury and HIV-related dementia. Increased public awareness that we can prevent some dementias—for example, by educating people about the effects of alcohol abuse on the brain—will help to reduce the numbers of people with these conditions. Interestingly, the addition of thiamine to flour, which was made mandatory in Australia in 1991, has helped to reduce rates of alcohol-related dementia, the effects of which are largely due to thiamine deficiency.[3]

Some people with younger onset dementia inherit it genetically from their parents. This can be the case in some instances of Alzheimer's Dementia or frontotemporal dementia. While many of the genetically inherited dementias have their onset under the age of 65, the overall risk remains relatively low. Genetic testing is available for those who are concerned that they might have an inherited dementia, or who fear that they might pass the illness on to their children. The pros and cons of any such testing need to be carefully thought through, and so it is important that genetic counselling is undertaken.

Due to the diversity of illnesses that fall under the umbrella of younger onset dementia, there are a number of different symptoms that individuals may initially report. In most cases, though, the symptoms experienced by a younger person with Alzheimer's Dementia are the same as for an older person with the illness. The main difference is that behavioural problems are more common in people aged under 65. This includes mood and personality changes such as depression, emotional flatness, becoming argumentative, and the development of obsessive behaviours such as hoarding.

Dementia in young people can be very difficult to diagnose. Some people wait for long periods before presenting to a doctor and, once they do, they are often offered more common explanations for their symptoms, such as stress, depression or menopause. People can therefore wait many years for their dementia to be accurately diagnosed. In some instances, a lack of diagnosis can lead to unnecessary divorce, financial hardship and family breakdown. We recommend that, regardless of age, people voice any concerns they have about their memory, thinking or behaviour to their doctor, and ask for their symptoms and treatment to be reviewed every six to 12 months. Additionally, we recommend that children be included, wherever possible, in discussions about the illness. Counselling may be of benefit to them, as well as to partners and other family members.

Due to their different stage in life and physical fitness, people with younger onset dementia don't fit in well with mainstream dementia services that are geared towards much older, and often more frail, persons. Younger people with dementia want services that cater for people in their age group and that focus upon energetic and fun activities, such as belly dancing, bushwalking or photography. Health services are starting to recognise the different needs of younger people with this illness and, fortunately, age-specific groups are beginning to appear.

An increased awareness that dementia can affect younger people will help break down the myth that dementia is an illness only of old age.

Dr Adrienne Withall
Research Fellow
Primary Dementia Collaborative Research Centre
School of Psychiatry, Faculty of Medicine
University of New South Wales

More information

For information about younger onset dementia support groups and services, please contact the National Dementia Helpline on 1800 100 500.

'Understanding younger onset dementia' (2008). *Alzheimer's Australia Quality Dementia Care Series.* This excellent and comprehensive article is available by entering 'understanding younger onset dementia' into the search box of <www.alzheimers.org.au>

Dr Withall is conducting a number of studies on patients and carers affected by younger onset dementia and can be contacted on (02) 9385 2597.

CHAPTER 6

Homocysteine: The new cholesterol?

What is homocysteine?

Up until the early 1900s, thousands of individuals would suffer a miserable death each year because of a condition called pernicious anaemia. Patients would exhibit telltale giant red blood cells under the microscope, lose weight, develop neurological problems and mental disturbances, and eventually die. This was until Drs Whipple, Minot and Murphy discovered in 1926 that the eating of raw liver could completely cure the disease. Dr Whipple had simulated anaemia by experimentally bleeding his dogs and noticed that the condition could be reversed after just a few liver-laden meals. The doctors were awarded the Nobel Prize for Medicine in recognition of their transformative discovery.

It wasn't until some 20 years later that researchers in the United States and United Kingdom isolated the vital curative ingredient in liver: **vitamin B12** (cobalamin). In 1955, the British chemist Dorothy Crowfoot Hodgkin discovered the full chemical structure of B12, which allowed for its mass production and the treatment of pernicious anaemia around the world. Her work was also recognised with a Nobel Prize.

At the same time, the pathologist Lucy Willis was working in India and discovered that extracts from yeast and green leafy vegetables could also reverse giant cell anaemias, including pernicious anaemia. In 1930 the extract from such green leafy foliages was identified and appropriately named **folate**.

These two great discoveries came together over the next 30 years to produce a clearer understanding of how our bodies produce one of its key amino acids—methionine—a critical building block of virtually every protein. In very simple terms, both folate and B12 are necessary parts of two complex biochemical cycles whose products include methionine and **homocysteine**. Part of this understanding came from clinical reports of young children born with very rare genetic abnormalities affecting a specific aspect of the folate and methionine biochemical cycles. These unfortunate children died young, with mental retardation and massive concentrations of homocysteine in the blood, even to the extent that it could be detected in their urine. Post mortems also revealed cholesterol plugs in their main cardiac arteries and strokes throughout their brains—the kind of brain changes normally only seen in individuals 70 years older.

Since a number of different genetic abnormalities related to folate and B12 metabolism all seemed to be leading to a common pathway—increased homocysteine and vascular disease—the pathologist Kilmer McCully proposed in 1969 that mild to moderate elevation of homocysteine, for whatever reason, might also contribute to vascular disease in the general population. Animal studies subsequently confirmed that either feeding or injecting homocysteine did indeed increase the severity of vascular disorders.

There is now a growing (but not universal) opinion among cardiologists that elevated homocysteine may be a risk factor for heart disease.[1] How or why this occurs, however, is far from clear. Some have suggested that homocysteine increases the propensity of our blood platelets to form sticky clots, or that homocysteine may itself be an intrinsic oxidative agent. (See Chapter 4 for information about oxidants and antioxidants.) As we may have come to expect from previous chapters, what seems to be bad for the heart is bad for the brain. When it comes to homocysteine, does the same rule apply?

High plasma homocysteine and brain disease

The links between high plasma homocysteine and heart disease have been replicated with cerebrovascular disease, and stroke in particular. The very large and influential Framingham Study in the United States monitored a group of almost 2,000 initially healthy older individuals and analysed which factors were independently predictive of having a stroke.[2] They found that individuals with high homocysteine levels were 1.8 times more likely to have a stroke during the follow-up period of ten years than were those with low homocysteine levels.

High homocysteine levels in the healthy population have also been associated with increased frequency and severity of white matter disease in the brain and more overall brain shrinkage, including shrinkage of the hippocampus, the memory structure known be particularly susceptible in Alzheimer's Disease. Professor Perminder Sachdev, Director of the Neuropsychiatric Institute in Sydney, was part of a team (with myself as a lowly research assistant) that initially noted the link between high homocysteine and brain shrinkage in otherwise normal older individuals.[3] These findings, along with many other similar studies, started researchers wondering whether homocysteine may also have a causal role in the development of dementia.

Is there a further link to dementia?

If high homocysteine levels increase our chances of developing heart disease, or experiencing a stroke and brain shrinkage, does it also increase our chances of developing dementia? On this question, results have been less clear-cut. The large Framingham study found that those with homocysteine levels in the highest

25 per cent had double the risk for dementia over the eight years of follow-up. At least two other large longitudinal studies have replicated similar results[4]; however, the Washington Heights–Columbia Aging Project, a large and respected longitudinal study, failed to find a similar association.

Interestingly, in those with dementia, high plasma homo-cysteine scores correspond with lower cognitive performance.[5] Indeed, in general, dementia patients typically have a higher homocysteine profile than comparable non-demented individuals.

More recent results have extended the association between homocysteine and cognitive function to the normal older population. One study found that cognitive differences between those with low homocysteine levels versus those with the highest 25 per cent of readings was equivalent to 4.2 years of ageing.

Evidence from biological studies suggests a multitude of ways that high homocysteine could promote the development of dementia. One mechanism may be the promotion of blockages in the vascular system, including the cerebrovascular system, leading to loss of proper brain blood flow, stroke, and so Vascular Dementia. Alternatively, high-homocysteine diets have been shown to increase the production of beta-amyloid production in animal models of AD. This result raises the issue of whether homocysteine has a starring role in the development of Alzheimer's Dementia.

Yet, there now appears to be a growing list of agents that increase amyloid production in these genetically engineered AD animals. The fact that they have been specifically designed to pump out pathological proteins may mean they are overly sensitive to *any* manipulation a researcher may make. For the moment, the bottom line appears to be that these animal 'models' of AD are still not model animal citizens when it comes to predicting what will work in human clinical trials. Hence, we can't be sure if this kind of evidence has any bearing on whether high homocysteine is causing dementia in humans.

Another problem is that high homocysteine levels aren't particularly specific to dementia or AD. In a series of older psychiatric patients, reduced B12 or folate levels were observed in many individuals with different diagnoses. So, could those with dementia just not be eating properly, leading to insufficient folate and B12 levels and hence *hyperhomocysteinemia* (high blood homocysteine)? Again, the data is contradictory.

Some studies suggest that raised homocysteine occurs in the context of general nutritional deficits; others indicate quite the opposite. It has also been put forward that dietary intake of B12 and folate may be perfectly adequate in late life; however, the high rate of atrophic gastritis (chronic inflammation of the lining of the stomach) with ageing could mean that these vitamins are not properly absorbed, and thus lead to raised homocysteine. Even still, increased homocysteine has been documented in older individuals with perfectly normal B12 and folate blood levels, and so the key issue remains: does lowering homocysteine improve our brain health? To address this question, we need to look at the results from clinical trials that have tried lowering homocysteine levels.

Clinical trials of B12 and folate

High homocysteine levels can be reduced surprisingly easily by simply eating more folate and B12. Even modest increases in folate/B12 can significantly reduce plasma homocysteine levels, even if these vitamins are in the normal range to start with. So, do clinical trials of B12/folate that reduce elevated homocysteine also end up reducing vascular disease, stroke and dementia?

This question aims to address the final and most challenging issue for homocysteine and its relationship to dementia (one that you will have noticed keeps cropping up). Chicken or egg? Cause or effect? Is homocysteine part of the process that ends up in dementia, so that by correcting it early we prevent the disease; or is it in fact a risk *marker*, telling us that 'Yes, this person's brain is under attack'? You may recall that a similar situation arose when we considered the link between oxidative stress and dementia in Chapter 4—risk factor or risk marker? Whenever this situation arises, clinical trials are needed to adjudicate.

Overall, the results have been disappointing. It seems that, as in the case for antioxidants and for cholesterol-lowering statins, the epidemiological and biological relationships with dementia—while promising—have led to a therapeutic dead end. Let's break it up into four groups of evidence.

1. Prevention of heart disease

Homocysteine was first linked to increased heart disease, so treatment with folate/B12 should work in this area, if at all. A major recent systematic review of all clinical trials, however, has failed to show that starting B12/folate supplements has any scientifically meaningful effects on rates of heart disease.[6]

2. Prevention of stroke

Five major clinical trials (each with more than 1,000 participants) have tested to see whether reduction of homocysteine through B12/folate supplementation has an effect on the occurrence of new strokes. Four out of five found no effects, and one found a minor effect. Overall, the evidence suggests that lowering homocysteine is unlikely to produce a meaningful effect on risk for stroke.

3. Treatment of dementia

A handful of small trials have tested whether B12/folate supplementation is of use in individuals with established dementia. These have been brought together in a meta-analysis, which is a method for mathematically combining results across different studies. The meta-analysis found no overall effect.[7]

4. Prevention of dementia: Trials under way

A number of large studies primarily designed to test for the prevention of stroke are also looking at whether lowering homocysteine can help prevent the development of dementia. They include the large Australian-based VITATOPS (Vitamins to prevent stroke) and US VISP (Vitamin intervention for stroke prevention) studies, which have been tracking individuals who were initially cognitively intact, and the VITACOG (Homocysteine and B vitamins in cognitive impairment) study that enrolled individuals with **Mild Cognitive Impairment** (MCI).

Results have been both interesting and perplexing. In an enormous effort, VITATOPS recruited over 8000 participants with a history of stroke from across 20 countries, and in 2010 reported that whilst B-vitamin supplementation was effective at lowering homocysteine, it had no effect on preventing heart attack, stroke or vascular death. On the other hand, VITACOG focused on the effect of both folate and B-vitamins in individuals with cognitive difficulties. One of the main outcomes of interest had been designed to be cognitive, and on this front results were negative – vitamin supplementation did not change the rate of decline in cognitive function. But interestingly, a substudy used consecutive brain scans to find that such vitamin supplementation protected the hippocampus from shrinkage. The VITACOG trial therefore presents a conundrum: lowering homocysteine with folate and B-vitamins may help protect the memory centre in the brain from atrophy, but does not seem to have an effect on cognitive function. A possible explanation is that perhaps a stronger dose of vitamins is necessary for prevention of cognitive decline, or the vitamins need to be taken much earlier in the process for a longer time period[8]. The relative importance of folate versus B-vitamins is also not clear. Obviously, much further research is required in this area.

Overall, it seems that the intense early interest by the medical community in homocysteine as a risk factor for heart disease, stroke and dementia is now somewhat clouded. However, since publication of the first edition of this book, the VITACOG study has changed my thinking about raised homocysteine.

Lesson #4: *Whilst there is no clear evidence that lowering elevated homocysteine levels reduces one's risk for dementia or stroke, it may possible have a beneficial effect on brain structure. Since dietary supplementation with folate and B-vitamins is quite safe and low-cost, these vitamins can be considered to possibly promote brain health when homocysteine is abnormally high.*

IN FOCUS Caring for a loved one with dementia at home: Advice from an expert

In this special section, Professor Henry Brodaty AO, an international authority on clinical care for individuals with dementia, covers a range of important issues for those currently—and those considering—caring for a loved one with dementia at home.

Supporting the person with dementia

The journey of dementia starts well before diagnosis. Knowing what to expect and how to cope can ease this difficult and, at times, emotionally fraught voyage.

Something has changed?

Usually there are subtle changes before anyone realises that something serious is happening to your loved one. They seem different—perhaps more stubborn, more irritable—and appear to be coping less well. They are forgetting messages, not completing tasks, stumbling over words and misunderstanding complex concepts. You put it down to stress, but you have a nagging worry that there is something more sinister behind their behaviour. Everyone talks about Alzheimer's Disease, but are you being neurotic in worrying? If your concerns persist and especially if the symptoms progress, an assessment, initially with your loved one's general practitioner, is warranted.

Seeing the doctor

You and your loved one should be clear that you want to have an assessment to explain the loss of memory, word-finding difficulties or behavioural changes. (Note that memory loss isn't always the first symptom of some types of dementia.) After taking the patient's history, performing a physical examination, and possibly arranging some blood tests and a brain scan, the GP may recommend seeing a specialist such as a neurologist, a psychiatrist with a special interest in memory problems, a geriatrician or a Memory Disorders Clinic.

Having received an assessment, people with cognitive complaints have a right to know, and a right *not* to know, whether their diagnosis is or is not dementia. The skill of the clinician is to give just the right level of information according to the wishes and needs of the patient and family.

You will want to know what the diagnosis is, how certain the diagnosis is, what can be done to help, and what is the outlook or prognosis. While it is usually best to be frank in discussing the diagnosis with the affected person, this should be done sensitively, breaking the news by degrees, respecting the person's emotional state and ensuring optimal timing.

A number of practical measures should be considered and acted upon at, or shortly after, diagnosis:

- *Legal.* It is prudent to arrange an enduring power of attorney, enduring guardianship and advance directives while your loved one is competent. Power of attorney gives a trusted person (or combination of persons) the right to act on behalf of another person in matters of finance or estate. In a parallel fashion, guardianship allows another person to make decisions about services, accommodation and health; power of attorney does *not* include these decision-making rights. In some jurisdictions, the power of attorney and guardianship orders become invalid when the person giving these powers loses competency *unless* a clause is endorsed stating that it should endure even if the donor loses competency. The person allocating these powers can stipulate that they should be triggered only if and when he or she loses legal competency.
- *Financial.* It is wise to consider the financial implications and to plan for the future.
- *Life planning.* This might be the time to take that overseas holiday or to reconsider moving to a retirement village. Will there be enough supports in the future? Will you be close to family? Or should you move now, while the

person is relatively intact cognitively and can adjust to new surroundings?

- *Driving.* This is always a contentious issue that requires a delicate negotiation; it is not only your loved one's safety that is at risk, but also the safety of others on the road. If in doubt, a driving test is recommended. Remember that doctors are legally required to recommend cancellation of a licence if they have concerns about safety.

- *Work.* If your loved one is still working, is this feasible and safe? Is it possible for them to transfer to a position with more supervision and less responsibility? In general, you and your loved one should plan on continuing as normal a life as possible.

A frequent dilemma that you may face is whether to tell family and friends about the diagnosis. Benefits of informing others include the possibility of gaining more support, the release from the stress of trying to hide the problem from others, and the increased potential for arranging compensatory strategies. Detriments are the fear of stigma and of being shunned, and your loved one feeling a loss of self-esteem. In practice, as most people close to the person with early dementia are aware that something is amiss and are unsure how to handle the increasing difficulties, it is best to be open.

There are medications available for Alzheimer's Disease. (See the discussion of cholinesterase inhibitors and *ginkgo biloba* in Chapter 4.)

General health should be attended to: blood pressure, cholesterol, fasting blood sugar, regular physical exercise, mental stimulation and social engagement.

Strategies can be devised to compensate for cognitive deficits. An occupational therapy assessment at home (if available), use of a diary, other memory aids, clocks with the day and date displayed, and establishment of routines can all be helpful.

At diagnosis the amount of information can be overwhelming. Ask for a written summary of the diagnosis, plans of management and prognosis. Is there a telephone number for further contact? Can you have a follow-up appointment?

Your goal is to become the expert on how best to support your loved one. To do this, you should become as knowledgeable as you can about the condition. Use the internet, contact Alzheimer's Australia (1-800-100-500 or <www.alzheimers.org.au>) or the corresponding organisation in other countries. (A list is available from Alzheimer's Disease International, <www.alz.co.uk>.) With your loved one take advantage of a free seven-week course called 'Living with

Memory Loss', conducted one morning a week by Alzheimer's Australia.

Your overarching aim is to maintain the best quality of life for you and your loved one. A diagnosis doesn't change a person's life from one day to the next. The prognosis for most dementias, such as Alzheimer's Disease, is slow deterioration over a number of years. Loss of short-term memory doesn't equate to loss of the ability to enjoy life, to receive and give love to others, and to have fun.

Early stages

People with dementia should be offered continuing support and regular appointments. They may want to discuss their frustrations and learn about strategies for coping with their cognitive decline. A meeting with others with similar problems can be helpful, although people differ in their preferences for talking with others. Online support for and by people with dementia is available through Dementia Advocacy and Support Network International <www.dasinternational.org>.

Some people with dementia readily accept their diagnosis, but others stubbornly deny there is a problem. Recognise that such denial may be a form of self-protection by your loved one. It is best to try to deal with the underlying anxiety, to emphasise your loved one's strengths, and to build on strategies to compensate for weaknesses. A psychologist may help if your loved one is depressed or anxious.

Middle stages

As dementia progresses, your loved one will become increasingly dependent on you. At first this might be for more complex processes such as managing finances, taking medication, transport, shopping and cooking. Later, dependency extends to prompting, then assistance with, bathing, dressing and toileting.

A dilemma that you may face is maintaining an adult–adult relationship with your loved one while simultaneously taking on more of a caring role. It is important to continue to communicate as equals, and not to talk down to your loved one or to become parental in your manner.

Behavioural and psychological symptoms frequently emerge as dementia progresses. Examples include depression, agitation, aggression, delusions of theft or infidelity, hallucinations, wandering, constant questioning and shadowing (of you). The reasons for these behaviours are complex and are often unique to your loved one. It is important to understand what underlies these symptoms. *Listen to the music, not the words* is a useful aphorism. It is easier to help if you can understand the underlying insecurity or other cause driving the behaviour. Here are two examples:

Your loved one constantly and repetitively asks to go home and is not quietened by your repeated reassurances, often at increasing volume, that 'You ARE home!'. The underlying issue is that your loved one is feeling insecure, even though in his or her own home. Rather than repeated verbal reassurances, a response at an emotional level, such as an affectionate hug, is more likely to make your loved one feel more secure.

Your loved one accuses you of stealing treasured valuables. You may feel hurt and even angry, but if you understand that your loved one has lost confidence and feels insecure, and as a result clings to and hides valuables but later forgets where, your reactions can be more supportive.

Late stages

As your loved one becomes even more dependent for basic care over more and more hours each day, the need for help from others becomes more pressing. Such support can come from your family and friends, and from community services such as community nurses or aged care workers who can assist with dressing, washing and toileting, or provide companionship to give you a break.

Residential care placement

Eventually, your loved one may be admitted into residential care—for example, into a nursing home. For a person with failing cognition to be placed in a strange environment, cut off from familiar orientating cues and family and friends, can be a frightening experience. It is best if you can prepare your loved one by arranging frequent visits before admission, continuing contact with family and friends after admission, and displaying mementos, photographs and personal memorabilia in the room in order to give it a sense of familiarity and homeliness.

You may feel guilt, which may sometimes be exacerbated by relatives' comments that you have let your loved one down. In fact, your loved one's quality of life can be improved and, freed from the relentless drudgery of daily basic care, you can spend more time engaging in enjoyable activities with them.

Support for you

You are a carer

As well as being a partner or child of your loved one, you have now assumed a new role, carer (also called caregiver). You are not alone in being unprepared for this; it creeps up, rather than being thrust on you, and gradually you realise, like the frog in the saucepan of water on the boil, how it has changed your life and your relationship.

What are the effects of being a carer?

You are more likely to experience psychological distress, such as depression, physical ill health, social isolation and financial hardship, than if you were not a carer. If you have poor health—physically or psychologically—you will experience even greater stress. If you have high blood pressure, this can be exacerbated. *You are the most important medicine for your loved one*, and so it is crucial that you look after your own physical and psychological health.

You are more likely to be stressed if your loved one is behaviourally disturbed, if you had a poor relationship before the onset of dementia, if your own psychological health is fragile, if you don't face up to the issues and find ways to deal with them, if you have few supports or if you don't know what to do.

It is important for you to find out as much information as you need about the diagnosis and how to manage. Seek out books, videotapes or CDs, websites and your local Alzheimer's Association support group. Ask for regular counselling or appointments with your doctor, social worker or Alzheimer's Australia counsellor if you feel you need it. Attend to the practical matters listed above. Don't be afraid to ask for help, to involve your family members and friends—those that are the busiest are often best able to assist.

Paradoxically, as your loved one declines further, care may become easier as the demands become more physical, rather than emotional, and many behavioural problems may subside. On the other hand, the need for constant supervision, the constant 'shadowing', and the lack of opportunity for individual relaxation can be extraordinarily taxing. You will only need to ask in order to receive more community care, and more frequent and longer periods of residential respite care.

In Australia, Aged Care Assessment Teams (ACATs) assess people with dementia to ascertain what levels of community support can be provided, which can range from a Community Aged Care Package (CACP) offering about six hours per week to an Extended Aged Care in the Home Package (EACH) equivalent to about three hours per day.

Positive effects of being a carer

There are rewards in providing care to your loved one, though these vary considerably with each family. They may include the fulfilment that you have been able to reciprocate a lifetime of mutual care, knowing that your loved one would have done the same for you if the situation were reversed, satisfaction that you have provided love and care as best you can, and perhaps a sense of altruism and even heightened spirituality.

There are moments of humour as well as agony. Dementia can bring families together to combat the effects of the disease. Many people with dementia remain in good spirits through most of their disease.

Carers and the law

As your loved one loses competency, you will assume greater responsibility and become their legal proxy. This includes giving informed consent for medications, or for participation in research, managing finances, and arranging and agreeing to services.

Conclusions

Looking after a loved one during the 'journey of dementia' presents new challenges throughout the course of the disease. Knowledge, preparation, and asking for and receiving help from family, friends and professional services can make the journey less demanding. There are also positive rewards from providing care to a loved one.

Websites

Alzheimer's Australia: <www.alzheimers.org.au>

Alzheimer's Disease International: <www.alz.co.uk>

Alzheimer's UK: <www.alzheimers.org.uk>

Dementia Advocacy and Support Network International (for people with dementia): <www.dasninternational.org>

References

1. H. Brodaty, A. Green and L-F. Low. Family Carers for People with Dementia, in J. O'Brien, D. Ames and A. Burns (eds), *Dementia*, 3rd edition (London: Arnold, 2005), pp. 118–31.

2. H. Brodaty and K. Berman. Interventions for Family Caregivers of People with Dementia, in R.T. Woods and L. Clare (eds), *Handbook of Clinical Psychology of Ageing*, 2nd edition (Chichester, UK: John Wiley & Sons, 2008), pp. 549–69.

3. B. Draper. *Dealing with Dementia* (Sydney: Allen & Unwin, 2005).

Professor Henry Brodaty AO

Aged Care Psychiatry

Prince of Wales Hospital &

Primary Dementia Collaborative Research Centre

School of Psychiatry, University of New South Wales

CHAPTER 7

Use it or lose it
Part 1: The science

What do you think happens to older mice if we apply the 'use it or lose it' principle? Interestingly, behavioural scientists have been testing the effects of environmental enrichment on rodents for more than 40 years and have amassed a wealth of data. **Environmental enrichment** involves putting mice in a larger cage with lots of toys, mazes, tunnels and running wheels for their exploration and use, as well as with more fellow animals for interaction. Mice in enrichment studies definitely have a better lifestyle and quality of life than their unenriched counterparts!

The most emphatic result to emerge from these studies is that enrichment improves mouse performance on almost any test we care to devise. If we take memory, for example, a few months of enrichment increases memory performance by 30–40 per cent. Similar improvements are also seen in tests of agility, problem solving and reaction to stress.

But what biological changes underlie these functional benefits? This has been of particular interest to me, ever since I first sensed that the link between mental activity and reduced dementia risk might be a compelling one. I have long wondered: 'How can this be? How can the simple act of thinking change the course of something as biologically tangible as dementia?'

Review of this area led me to conclude that enrichment caused not one, but a number of distinct biological changes within the brain.[1] These range in both scale and time frame. The type and nature of proteins that are pumped out by individual brain cells, for example, alter within the first few hours of enrichment. On the other hand, a few weeks of 'cognitive training' can produce major changes to the pattern of metabolic activation seen across the whole brain.

In this chapter, we will focus on what may underlie the 'use it or lose it' effect. In the following chapter, we will then make some practical suggestions for activities that will maximise your chances of avoiding dementia.

The neuro-revolution: How neurogenesis and neural stem cells may offer hope for treating dementia

For over a hundred years we have been taught at school and university that you can't grow new brain cells as an adult, right? Wrong! One of the biggest revolutions in neuroscience has been the discovery that the creation of new neurons—a process termed **neurogenesis**—is, in fact, a normal part of brain biology. Every day, even in old age, we all make around 5,000 new brain cells! All the available evidence points to the inescapable fact that neurogenesis is a lifelong process.

Neurogenesis does not, however, favour all parts of the brain equally. Two parts of the brain seem to specialise in this process. The first is an area called the *subventricular zone*, a thin strip of tissue that surrounds the ventricles—which are the fluid-filled cavities in the centre of the brain. Remarkably, new brain cells produced as a result of neurogenesis in this region migrate across half the length of the brain, via a well-worn pathway, to mature in the olfactory bulb (smell centre) at the very frontal tip of the brain. This phenomenon is one of the most well-conserved in nature, occurring in animals as diverse as lobsters, birds and humans. Why this should occur remains a mystery, since there doesn't seem to be a clear correlation between the level of neurogenesis along this pathway and our ability to smell.

The second main zone for neurogenesis is in the hippocampus—a pair of folded-up, sausage-shaped structures near the base of the brain. The hippocampus is probably the most studied brain region in neuroscience, since for decades it has been implicated in memory—in particular, the formation of new memories for where things lie in relation to the surrounding environment (visuospatial memory). It is no coincidence, for example, that some Alzheimer pathology starts in the hippocampus at the same time that patients start to suffer from visuospatial memory problems.

Unlike the subventricular zone, hippocampal neurogenesis starts and ends in the one brain region. New neurons form, mature and interconnect with established neurons in the local neighbourhood. This occurs every day and apparently doesn't end until *we* do. So why, one may well ask, do our hippocampi not enlarge to the point where they eventually take up our whole skull? There are probably a couple of reasons. First, the brain cells in the hippocampus are a sensitive bunch. For example, thousands of neurons can die off when we are stressed and produce the stress hormone **cortisol**. When we are feeling highly stressed, we do seem to think less clearly and tend to forget even simple things. High levels of cortisol in our blood at those times can act like a mild brain poison. So, in order to keep the general number of cells in the hippocampus relatively constant, we actually need a source of new brain cells to replenish those that are 'lost in combat'. Second, most of the new cells that are born every day have a short life span, with only a small percentage going on to mature and integrate into the existing circuitry.

It seems that in order to maintain a status quo of sorts, we are continually generating in the hippocampus many more brain cells than we actually need, with most dying off and those useful ones hanging around to serve their purpose. What that purpose actually is remains unclear. Competing theories suggest that neurogenesis may be required for proper memory function, or to regulate our moods, or that it is just an incidental process of little consequence.

The effect of Alzheimer's on neurogenesis is quite interesting. We know that AD pathology begins in the hippocampus, and the orthodox 'amyloid' theory suggests that this is the prime cause for the high levels of neural loss witnessed in this brain area (see Chapter 2). So one might expect reduced neurogenesis as well. In fact, what researchers have found is *increased* neurogenesis in the hippocampus. The interpretation which best fits is that, while AD definitely leads to loss of brain cells in the hippocampus in general, it *doesn't* seem to negatively affect the machinery of neurogenesis, and so our bodies appear to be trying to compensate for this neural loss by producing more new brain cells. Unfortunately in AD, any such compensation is ultimately destined to failure, because the magnitude of cell loss is in the end simply too great.

A final part to the enigma of neurogenesis is the precise origin of these new brain cells. In general, the 'no new brain cells' orthodoxy was actually pretty close to the mark: the vast majority of our brain cells cannot divide and replicate beyond the early period of life. That is why we cannot, to any significant degree, regenerate new brain areas after a traumatic brain injury, or following a stroke or other major brain insult. However, in those 'privileged' areas such as the hippocampus, obviously some cells *are* dividing and replicating well into our adult life. Because these cells can self-renew almost indefinitely, and generate not only neurons, but also other types of brain cells, they are referred to as **neural stem cells** (NSCs).

A full discussion of the fascinating area of NSCs really requires its own book, but suffice to say that it is one of the most promising areas of neuroscience. Part of the attraction is the clinical potential: if we could harness the power of NSCs *and therefore artificially augment neurogenesis* we might be able to treat, and even reverse, those major neurological diseases that afflict humankind, such as spinal cord injury, Parkinson's disease, stroke and, of course, dementia. The other facet is their biological charisma; NSCs can be generated from brain tissue, as one may expect, but also from embryonic tissue, bone marrow and even adult skin! Stem cells are therefore quite 'plastic' and slippery to define, control and conceptualise. Researchers around the world, including myself, are now racing to develop technologies and therapeutic strategies based on NSCs for the treatment of dementia.[2] However, it could be said that we are just at ground level and eventually need to get to the tenth floor. Associate Professor Kuldip Sidhu of the Faculty of Medicine at the University of New South Wales, and one of Australia's leading stem cell scientists, summarises it in this way:

> With the death of so-called 'no neurogenesis dogma' during the last decade or so, there has been a spurt of research activity relating to neurodegenerative disease and neural stem cells. Recent breakthroughs in stem cell research have opened up new hope to use cell replacement therapy for many debilitating human diseases like Alzheimer's, Parkinson's and spinal cord injury. Before harnessing the full potential of these stem cells in regenerative medicine, however, their safety and efficacy need to be established. I have no doubts in my mind that tomorrow's medicine will be driven by stem cell-based therapies in one form or the other. There is a great hope to alleviate human suffering with this cutting-edge stem cell research that is emerging rather rapidly.[3]

Mental activity promotes brain growth in adulthood

One of the most reliable findings in the neurogenesis area is that placing animals in an enriched environment increases their numbers of new brain cells. Professor Gerd Kempermann, of the Center for Regenerative Therapies in Dresden, Germany, was one of the first to show this result, and he extended his findings specifically to include ageing rodents.[4] He found that the survival of new neurons in the brains of older rats was augmented more than threefold when placed in a more stimulating environment, increasing from 8 per cent in the standard condition to 26 per cent in the enrichment condition. Furthermore, this effect was specifically in the hippocampus. It is therefore quite possible that staying mentally active in later life could have a beneficial effect on neurogenesis and therefore build up a greater 'buffer' of brain cells compared to otherwise.

One of the problems with the idea of building a neural buffer through mental activity comes down to numbers. If we assume that we generate 5,000 new neurons a day and that only 10 per cent survive for any length of time, that equates to 500 additional neurons; if we then assume that mental activity increases this by five times, that's 2,500 *additional* neurons that otherwise would not be there. The problem is that early AD involves the loss of tens of millions of neurons in the hippocampus alone, apart from the rest of the brain. What difference could 2,500 new neurons make against the decimation brought on by AD?

While basic arithmetic like this is, of course, highly simplistic, it does highlight an important issue yet to be resolved. An alternative explanation that I find even more attractive stems from the strong effect which mental activity has on synapses, the *links between neurons*. In some mysterious way, all conscious activities—from the redolent pleasure of tasting a quality shiraz, to our most fraught internal dialogues—are intimately and directly related to the transfer of biological information among our brain cells. In many ways, loss of brain cells isn't half as important as the loss of communicating pathways between brain cells. To take one extreme, what would be the point of a neuron if it didn't communicate with another, and that one with another, and so forth? At the other extreme one can imagine a network of neurons with many redundant connections, so that even if one is killed off, parallel pathways are available that keep the network's function stable. Whenever we begin to talk of the brain in terms of communication, information transfer and networks, we are by definition relying on the preservation and integrity of our synapses.

As you may have guessed, researchers have specifically examined the effect of enrichment on synaptic numbers and the results are startling. Twelve months of enrichment increases synaptic numbers by, on average, 200–300 per cent. Given that *even a single neuron can possess over 10,000 synapses*, mental activity could potentially lead to astonishing elevations in synaptic connections between brain cells.

Given these considerations, it is no surprise that of all the cellular measures that scientists have looked at in people with

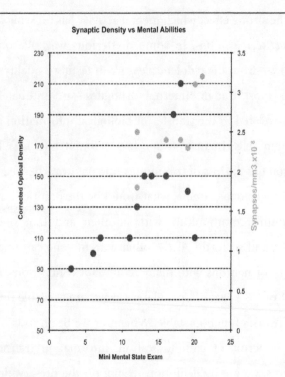

Figure 5 Synaptic density versus mental abilities
The graph shows the relationship between synaptic density (measured in two different ways in two different studies shown in dark and light dots on the *y*-axes), and overall mental abilities measured by the Mini-Mental State Examination (MMSE) on the *x*-axis in people with dementia. Normal healthy older people tend to score in the range of 24–30/30 on the MMSE. In the graph the highest MMSE score is 20, confirming that all these individuals had dementia. The overall correlation of r=0.71 signifies a high level of association between these two variables—i.e., between mental ability in dementia and synaptic densities. (*Note:* This simple graph summarises the work of a team of people conducted over a period of more than a year.)

Sources: S. Scheff and D.A. Price. Synaptic pathology in Alzheimer's disease: a review of ultrastructural studies. *Neurobiology of Aging* (2003) 24:1029–46; and R. Terry, et al. Physical basis of cognitive alterations in Alzheimer's disease: synapse loss is the major correlate of cognitive impairment. *Annals of Neurology* (1991) 30:572–80.

dementia, it is synaptic numbers that has the strongest relationship with mental function. Two different groups have now reported findings indicating that more than half the variability in mental performance between individuals with dementia is due to their synaptic numbers. So, if on a graph we plot a person's mental ability on the *x*-axis, and their synaptic numbers on the *y*-axis, the dots would form a very neat upward-sloping diagonal line, as shown in Figure 5. In other words, the more synapses you have, the less cognitive *problems* you are likely to experience, and vice versa.

I therefore believe that one of the most important effects of mental activity is to increase the number of synapses in different brain regions. By keeping mentally active, we can build up a 'reserve' or buffer of synapses, so that if a disease such as AD does strike, we can maintain our cognitive abilities for longer than might otherwise have been the case.

The bulging brain versus the shrinking brain

We have discussed how enrichment can produce startling effects on fundamental neurological processes such as neurogenesis and synaptic numbers. Amazingly, enrichment can also increase the mass and size of the brain! Researchers in the 1970s noted that three months of a more stimulatory environment caused a 7 per cent increase in an animal's brain weight and size. Perhaps even more amazingly, similar results have been found with humans. One group found that five weeks of training in ball juggling not only improved their repertoire of party tricks, but also caused parts of their brain to swell by almost 5 per cent. A few weeks after the end of training, these areas had returned to normal. Similar effects have also been seen after a few weeks of **aerobic exercise**.

How about the hippocampus, that part of the brain where all the action seems to be? We know that the hippocampus shrinks, usually by about 2–4 per cent each year, after the age of 60. As part of the Sydney Stroke Study, led by Professors Perminder Sachdev and Henry Brodaty of the University of New South Wales, we directly examined the link between rates of hippocampal shrinkage and people's mental activity levels. Surprisingly, the effect was quite strong. After careful measurement of individuals' brain scans, those with high levels of mental activity lost 3.6 per cent of their hippocampal volume over three years, whereas individuals with low levels of mental activity lost more than two times as much (8.3 per cent) over the same time frame (Figure 6).

Loss of hippocampal tissue is a very strong indicator of underlying AD pathology; when severe, it can even help to predict whether an individual will develop dementia in the future. The implication of these results is therefore clear: a high level of mental activity is linked to less hippocampal shrinkage, and less hippocampal shrinkage minimises your chances of developing dementia.

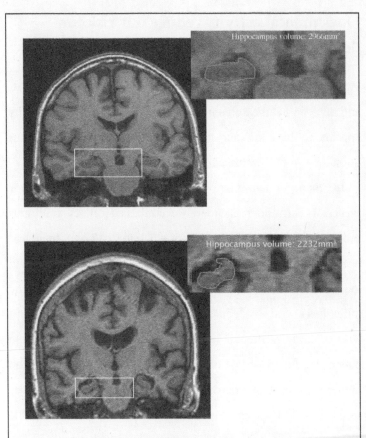

Figure 6 Hippocampal shrinkage and mental activity levels

These MRI brain scans show a section of the brain looking straight on. The images in the upper panel are from an older person with a high degree of lifelong complex mental activities (as measured by the LEQ—see panel at the end of Chapter 8), while the images in the lower panel are from an older person with much lower levels of complex mental activities. Even to the naked eye the difference in volume of the hippocampus (outlined under higher magnification) is obvious.

Source: From M. Valenzuela et al. 'Lifespan mental activity predicts rate of hippocampal atrophy'. *PLoS One* (2008) 3(7):e2598.

Does mental activity reduce our risk for dementia?

We have looked at the effects of enrichment on the brains of rats and mice, and at the different types of benefits that mental activity appears to have on our brains, but what about the obvious question—*does it change our risk for dementia?*

In 2006, in conjunction with my colleague and mentor Professor Perminder Sachdev, we embarked on an ambitious project to try to address this question. Up to that point, there had been hundreds of studies which, in one way or another, had looked at the link between the onset of new dementia and the individual's years of education, occupational complexity, and level of complex mental activities. After trawling through these papers, we finally settled on a group of 22 studies that met the highest scientific standards, which together had tracked over 29,000 individuals over an average of seven years. Combining this information in a meta-analysis (a formal mathematical method) had a major advantage, because a general truism in science is that the larger your sample size, the more accurate your results. When the result first came up on my computer I was astonished. *Individuals with higher levels of lifetime mental activity had a 46 per cent lower chance of developing dementia.* Basically, the rates of dementia in the high mental activities group were almost half that of the lower group.

Even more interesting was that this result seemed to stay consistent even in later life. That is to say, if we statistically adjust for someone's level of education or occupational complexity, the same result holds: high mental activity after retirement age is associated with a 40–50 per cent reduction in dementia risk. This is perhaps one of the most positive and empowering results in the field because, truly, it does seem to indicate that *it's never too late to change your mind!*

So, if you should find yourself in late life and you perhaps missed out on an advanced education, or a complex and mentally demanding career, *there is still hope.* All the indicators suggest that everyone has the chance to lower their risk for dementia by taking on complex, challenging and enjoyable mental pursuits *at any age.*

Of mice and men

While the results referred to above are all very good, could mental activity actually halt, or even reverse, the biological cascade that leads to Alzheimer's Disease itself? One of the more celebrated studies in the last few years has suggested just this. Sangram Sisodia and colleagues from the University of Chicago examined the effects of enrichment on mice that had been genetically modified so as to over-produce beta-amyloid plaques, which, as noted in Chapter 2, is one of the main pathological markers for

Alzheimer's Disease. They found that six months of enrichment led to a 50 per cent decline in the level of beta-amyloid build-up in these animals. Similar findings have been found by others; however, the results remain controversial because one group has failed to replicate the finding.

It is tempting to link the 50 per cent reduction in dementia risk that we found in our study, with the 50 per cent decline in AD pathology found in the enrichment studies, but this is a bridge too far. In the end, no amount of testing the effects of enrichment on mice (whether using natural or genetically modified 'AD mice') will put this matter to rest, because quite obviously mice are far from human. Mice don't naturally develop a parallel disease to AD, and when genetically modified to mimic certain aspects of the disease, they do so only in a piecemeal and clinically non-predictive fashion.

Moreover, there is a touch of circular logic to the whole enterprise: researchers start by assuming that a defect in (for example) beta-amyloid processing is the root cause of AD, then genetically modify the animal to replicate this effect, show that it exhibits behavioural problems, and then label the animal strain an 'AD model'. It is no surprise, then, that it is almost impossible to predict the results of human trials on the basis of results from transgenic AD mice. A particular truism comes to mind: When you only have a hammer, the whole world can appear a nail.

Clinical trials of mental activity

In order to establish that mental activity *can* alter one's risk for dementia, we must therefore turn to the results of human clinical trials. This is an area that is really beginning to heat up. Up until 2000, there was not a single such study in the science literature; now there are half a dozen.[5] Part of the interest in these studies is because commercial enterprises have begun to market 'mind games' with the promise of cognitive and brain benefits. (See the *In Focus* section at the end of this chapter.) The other reason is that there has been a general acknowledgement among doctors that *non-pharmacological preventative strategies* have a far more important place these days than simply relying on new wonder drugs to bail us out after the damage has been done.

None of the clinical trials reported so far were actually designed to answer the question whether mental activity can reduce one's risk for dementia. Rather, the studies have looked at the effect of different types of mental training on the *rate of cognitive decline*. The good news is that all have shown positive trends: mental training of one sort or another tends to slow the rate of cognitive decline over time. Indeed, when these trials are put together in a meta-analysis the overall effect is both strong and statistically significant. The bad news is that often the effects have been quite narrow; for example, training in solving puzzle X tended to boost puzzle X solving ability at a later point in time, but it didn't generalise to other cognitive abilities, such as solving puzzles Y and Z.

One of the largest clinical trials of its kind, the US-based ACTIVE study,[6] however, has injected new impetus into the area by showing a *generalised effect*. The researchers initially split 2,832 participants into four groups: ten weeks of memory training, reasoning training, mental speed training, or a wait-and-see control condition. Five years later they retested everyone and found that reasoning training had an enduring and scientifically robust effect on participants' ability to complete everyday tasks such as shopping, making meals, managing day-to-day finances, and so forth. In other words, just ten weeks of reasoning training had a positive and lasting effect five years later that generalised to basic living functions, those same basic functions which, when negatively affected, form one of the core criteria for a diagnosis of dementia (see Chapter 1).

We are therefore now tantalisingly close to establishing beyond a reasonable doubt that mental activity can indeed prevent dementia. The main problem with the ACTIVE (Advanced cognitive training for independent and vital elderly) trial, it seems, was that their volunteers were *in general* exceptionally high functioning even at the start of the study. The rate of change in cognitive and basic living functions was therefore just too low in the group as a whole. One could well ask, what is the point of beginning such an intervention if you are basically 100 per cent mentally okay to start with?

These issues have been addressed in a clinical trial currently under way, led by Professor Maria Fiatarone Singh of the University of Sydney, and in collaboration with myself and other researchers from around Australia, called the SMART trial (Study of Mental Activity and Regular Training). The purpose of the SMART trial is threefold. First, we aim to determine what type of activity is best for preventing dementia: mental activity, physical activity, or the combination of both mental and physical activity? Second, we are limiting entry to the trial to those individuals at high risk for dementia by virtue of a borderline result on a screening cognitive test. In this way, if our results are positive, they will be directly relevant to those people at most risk for getting dementia in the first place. Lastly, we will not only be looking at the effect of our training on dementia risk, but also on any underlying brain changes. We expect final results from the SMART trial to begin to be released in 2012. Stay tuned.

Conclusions

We have seen that evidence for mental activity playing a prominent role in dementia risk reduction is solid and continues to increase. This evidence ranges from a myriad of positive effects on the mouse brain, to documented brain health benefits in humans. In addition, an active mental lifestyle has been linked to decreased dementia risk across dozens of population studies, and these effects are beginning to be replicated in human clinical trials. The message is therefore consistent and clear:

Lesson #5: *There is a strong possibility that keeping mentally active reduces your risk for dementia.*

In the next chapter, we will see how best to convert this lesson into specific lifestyle recommendations. Real-life examples of activities that capture the power of the 'use it or lose it' principle will be offered, as well as being put under the microscope from a brain science perspective.

IN FOCUS Do 'brain gym' video games work?

To answer this question properly, we need to start by asking ourselves what we truly mean by *work*? What will be our yardstick for measuring the success, or otherwise, of the growing list of commercially available mental exercise games?

Some historical context is important. Psychologists have been studying the effects of 'brain training' of one sort or another in older persons for more than 20 years.[7] These exercises have generally been in 'paper and pencil' format, or via group classes led by an expert instructor. The results have been fairly consistent: just about *any type of memory training* helps to improve performance in the *trained task* in the *short term.*

So, the first important point is that no one has yet come up with a 'magic' memory exercise that is necessarily better than any other. Exercising your memory, in whatever form, seems to be the key. Therefore, I can see no reason for choosing one commercial package over another until comparative clinical trials have been reported.

Second, as discussed in this chapter, the problem of transfer of effect is critical. The reason most older people wish to do these exercises is in order to preserve their overall mental functions so that they can continue doing those things that are important to them—and so avoid dementia—as opposed to becoming the world's fastest person in matching letters to a pattern, or remembering the right square on a grid!

Commercial packages like to cite performance gains of 'so-many percentage points'. Yet, these are gains in performance on the same tasks the person has been performing for a number of months. It seems self-evident that you will get better and better at a task that you practise over and over. The other way of reporting results has been in terms of 'brain age', which is probably a nice marketing gimmick but is scientifically meaningless on an individual level.

The commercial packages are yet to demonstrate that, by using their technology to exercise your mind, a person's general cognitive abilities *and* everyday function are improved or maintained in the long term, relative to a randomised control group. As mentioned in this chapter, however, evidence of transfer of gain is emerging in clinical trials that have used more traditional training approaches. In principle, I can foresee that similar effects may be possible from computerised training programs. These trials need to be done.

Next, the durability of a protective effect is also important. Some products say in their *unpublished* 'validation studies' that one month's practice on their mind games led to improvements of 9–30 per cent *on these same tasks*. Yet, there is no reporting of whether these improvements are maintained after the person stops practising. Perhaps one is expected to continue doing these games forever? If this is the case, then I have low expectations. We know that people in general don't comply well to continuous lifestyle modification, even when their lives depend on it. Take, for example, adherence to a healthy diet; the benefits of this are common knowledge, yet the rates of diabetes and obesity continue to rise.

On the other hand, the ACTIVE clinical trial mentioned in this chapter found some modest *generalised* improvements in everyday functioning after ten weeks of traditional cognitive training *that persisted for five years*. This kind of long-term clinical trial of a *computerised* mental activity program is therefore sorely needed, not only for the reasons outlined already, but because these training programs have *one main advantage* over their traditional counterparts. This advantage is their ability to customise the difficulty level of the task to the individual, and to continue increasing difficulty levels over time as the person's performance improves.

One final issue to consider is the fascinating result from a research group which showed that, all things being equal, older individuals trained at home on a memory exercise *with their partner* did better than if they learned and practised it by themselves. So, as will be expanded on in the next chapter, having a colleague, friend or team-mate to complete the training with seems to be an advantage. In other words, a social dimension is as important as a cognitive dimension. Practising brain gym exercises alone on one's Nintendo or computer may therefore come with an 'opportunity cost' if it means that you start to neglect your social and physical activities.

It would appear that computerised mental exercise training therefore has some potential for reducing cognitive impairment and dementia in late life; however, these predictions remain to be scientifically validated, and the important issues of *transfer of effect* and *durability* of effect need to be addressed. As will be discussed in the next chapter, there are a number of alternatives to going out and buying a commercial brain gym package that may be just as effective, cheaper and much more fun!

CHAPTER 8

Use it or lose it
Part 2: The art

The *Three Keys* to dementia prevention

Members of the public often ask me, 'What activity will best help me to avoid dementia?' In reality, after meticulously surveying the international literature, I have to conclude that no one pursuit, hobby or pastime emerges as the optimal choice.

A pattern does emerge, however, in terms of those activities that are probably more effective than others. These sorts of activities have three essential ingredients in common. However, before we consider what can be thought of as the *Three Keys* of dementia prevention, it is worth mentioning one final rodent study.

As discussed in the previous chapter, enrichment involves moving an animal from its regular 'boring' home cage environment into one that is larger and generally more stimulating, with more housemates, toys, running wheels, mazes, and so forth. If we analyse this for a moment, we can see that the enrichment manipulation is actually composed of at least three sub-components: (1) a social intervention, because there are now more other housemates in one's immediate environment; (2) a physical intervention, because overall activity has been increased, particularly with the addition of running wheels; and (3) a cognitive component, due to the extra mental work involved in exploring new toys, mazes, and the like.

Professor Gary Arendash of the University of South Florida recognised the triple-pronged nature of traditional enrichment and, in a very clever piece of experimentation, attempted to tease these apart.[1] He began with genetically modified 'AD mice' and transferred them from standard housing into one of several different modified home environments. A 'social' group benefited solely from more cage-mates (but no running wheels or mazes and toys); the 'physical' group only had additional running wheels; and the 'cognitive' group only had mazes and toys. Interestingly, there was a fourth group with all three modifications—that is, those under the complete enrichment conditions. At the end of the study, three outcomes were measured that were of direct parallel relevance to humans with dementia: (1) development of AD pathology, (2) memory performance, and (3) synaptic numbers. The results from the study were clear-cut. While all the groups benefited to a certain extent compared to the standard housing group, only the *complete* enrichment group won the 'trifecta'—less AD pathology, improved memory scores and increased synaptic numbers!

What is surprising, and somewhat intellectually satisfying for someone like myself, is that a similar pattern emerges from human population research. Those older individuals who partake in activities with a social, physical and cognitive component tend to avoid dementia, compared to those involved in less complex or intense activity. Hence, the *Three Keys to maximising your chances of avoiding dementia are*: *ensure that you practise activities with a strong social, physical and cognitive component.*

Keen readers will appreciate that it is almost impossible to come up with a purely social activity that doesn't, for example, have some physical element. On the other hand, the art of socialising equally requires a lot of thinking, planning, reacting, predicting, and so on ... that is, cognition! This is beyond doubt. What I suggest, however, is that some activities have a stronger emphasis on all *Three Keys* than others, and it is these types of activities that we ought to be engaging in.

Let's get practical

We all are counselled and trained—even forced—to plan our retirement from a financial perspective. A central message from this book is that we should be paying just as much attention to planning our retirement from a 'healthy brain' perspective. What is the point of retiring with a healthy superannuation package at age 65, say, if we'll have become demented within five years or so?

An infinitely more positive scenario is that we are able to enjoy life to the fullest during our 20 or so post-retirement years. In order to do this, we need to replace the social, physical and cognitive activity that was an inherent part of our jobs—and which normally fills up to 50 per cent of our waking lives—with new activities that also have a social, physical and cognitive component. This is what I mean about planning our retirement from a 'healthy brain' perspective. What's more, we should be planning for this *now*.

I am not advocating that everyone should practise endless 'mind games', pump iron at the gym every day, and finish off with an evening mahjong session (but please feel free to go ahead if these activities appeal)! Any activities planned for your retirement need to be fun to *you*; they should bring *you* pleasure and enjoyment. *This is because, whatever the nature of the activities, they will more than likely need to be kept up for the rest of your life to ensure maximum effect against dementia.* So, here are some options and my analysis of each one.

1. Keep on working … and loving it

One option that is becoming more common is that we don't really retire: we just shift down to part-time and perhaps stop getting paid for it. This tends to happen to individuals who are particularly good at what they do, love doing it, and just don't want to stop. Sometimes they work as 'honorary' consultants (if not paid), or they move around their old industry as Mr or Ms Fixit, giving their expert advice on difficult problems. Not only is this a great approach from a 'healthy brain' perspective, but having these 'living treasures' at our disposal obviously also has enormous benefits both for the community and the economy.

The only downside to this approach is that, if our 'old' job was essentially intellectual in nature (as tends to be the case for these individuals), then we may neglect the physical and social keys. In this case, it is imperative that we supplement our semi-retired lifestyle with a new pastime or hobby to fill the gap.

One particularly innovative solution to emerge in recent years is an initiative by Brisbane businessman Ken Magoffin. He launched the website <www.greynomadsemployment.com>, which caters for the 'grey nomads'—the 50,000 or so Australian retirees who take to the road each year and spend their twilight years travelling around the country and the world. The idea behind the website is that if you're in this category and happen to find yourself in a rural or regional town for any length of time, there may by an opportunity to mix your R&R with a bit of opportunistic work on the side if there is a need for your skills or talents. Both travellers and employers can meet online via the website. It's a simple idea, but a powerful concept.

2. Fall in love again

Did you ever have a passion or hobby that a demanding work schedule, children, pets, grandparents, or just plain old life stopped you from pursuing? Well, retirement is your chance to fall in love with it all over again. The main thing to ensure is that all *Three Keys* are in play. And what if your chosen pastime is weak in terms of one of the *Three Keys*? Simple—just modify or supplement it.

Let's take one passion that many people develop and nurture throughout their lives: gardening. From my (very limited) experience, gardening certainly has a strong physical component. It also involves the cognitive key, with all the attendant planning, assessing, reading, comparing, and so forth. However, it isn't all that common that gardening involves socialising with others. My advice to gardening aficionados is therefore to join a gardening club, society, or volunteer community garden—as well as doing your own gardening at home—so that once a week or fortnight you have the chance to meet up with other garden lovers to discuss your garden, their garden, the latest trends and tips, upcoming gardening shows and events, and all the other things that people talk about and do when they get together. See, it's easy!

3. Time to get passionate

If the idea of continuing part-time work after retirement is about as appealing as developing a hernia, and you have never really had a hobby or pastime to speak of, *then you will definitely need to get passionate about something.* But, what? Here are four suggestions that handsomely satisfy the *Three Keys.*

LEARN TO DANCE

Professor Joe Verghese and colleagues published a report in the prestigious *New England Journal of Medicine* in 2003 on a study in which they tracked the mental health of 469 individuals over five years, specifically looking at participation in nine physical activities in order to determine if there was a link with dementia risk.[2] Guess which was the only exercise to predict reduced dementia risk? Yes, dancing!

Having been a keen salsa dancer since my university days, I really think dancing has a lot going for it. Let's analyse it from the *Three Keys* point of view. Obviously, taking dance classes and practising a partner-based dance is a social experience, so that's one big tick. Equally, it can be quite physical, as anyone who has spent a night dancing can confirm. That's a second big tick.

But what about the cognitive key? If you have never been to a dance class, then you may not realise that it can be mentally demanding. First, there is learning how to better control and coordinate your body, sometimes carrying out motions that you have never tried before. Next, there are the moves, complex sequences that need first to be put into short-term memory for reproduction during class, and then into longer-term memory so that you don't have to start over again at the next class. Over time, the effortful and deliberate retrieval of sequences from long-term memory becomes effortless actions under the control of automatic motor memory processes. And then there is the perception of beat and rhythm, the anticipation of one's partner's movements and intentions, and so on … It's no wonder that it's sometimes so hard to make it look easy! Learning to dance definitely has a strong cognitive component, and therefore this pastime more than adequately fulfils the *Three Keys*. Besides that, it is a lot of fun, often addictive for beginners, and you get to dance with beautiful people. Need I say more?

TAKE UP TAI CHI

Martial arts fulfil the *Three Keys* in many of the same ways as learning to dance. It is self-evidently a physical pursuit. There is also a strong social component—walk into any dojo, or martial arts school, and it is impossible not to notice the strong sense of camaraderie, insider jokes, backslapping and robust commentary. Inevitably, members of a school socialise after class or get together to celebrate events. It seems that enduring physical hardship together tends to bring about a special type of mateship. The cognitive component is also just as strong as in dance, because of the similar use of short- and long-term memory, which gradually transfers into motor memory. It's no surprise, then, that Bruce Lee was not only a phenomenal martial artist, but also an insightful philosopher[3] as well as being the Hong Kong cha-cha dance champion of 1958! Many martial arts also include drills where reaction time and speed are honed and optimised, a direct analogy to the speed-of-information processing training that can be found in many 'brain gym' video games (see *In Focus* in Chapter 7).

Now, a 'full contact' martial art may not be the best way to start in late life if you have never done anything like that before. There are many 'soft' martial arts to choose from, with all the same predicted brain health benefits. Tai Chi, for example, can eventually involve learning over 1,000 separate movements. I dare anyone to explain how this can be accomplished without a prodigious amount of memory training. Tai Chi also emphasises the regulation of breathing, in itself beneficial to general health, as well as being an extremely effective technique for countering stress. So, go out and try a martial art and you can become a *Master of the Three Keys Dementia-Busting System*!

SAIL AWAY

There are few things as satisfying in this world as putting up a sail, taming the wind and heading off across a shimmering sea. And what better time to learn and practise this skill than after retirement!

One of the reasons I love sailing so much is the almost sublime mix it provides of romanticism, hedonistic pleasure, physical prowess and intellectual challenge. If you are sailing with others, the physical and social keys are therefore well serviced. But where is the intellectual ingredient? It really depends on how deep you wish to go. If you are happy to take a back seat as a passenger, you could easily switch your brain to autopilot. However, if you are the skipper, or are starting training to become one, then there is an almost endless list of issues, knowledge, skills and rich history to explore. Even a humble leisure cruise around a protected waterway such as Sydney Harbour would require knowledge of watercraft safety, basic boat handling, emergency procedures, basic radio control, charting a passage, navigation, reading a compass, and so on. The more advanced you become, the more there is to know. For instance, Ocean Masters need to be capable of navigating by the stars!

CUNNING RUNNING

I hadn't even heard of this activity until Associate Professor Sue Kurrle, an inspirational geriatrician based at Hornsby Hospital in Sydney, introduced me to one of her favourite pastimes. More formally known as orienteering, cunning running is a competitive sport in which individuals or teams go off into the bush with a map and compass in hand, and then race the clock to get from A to B in the quickest time possible. While en route, competitors need to work out on-the-fly if a more direct route over possibly tricky or steep terrain is likely to be faster or slower than a more circuitous route over even ground. Basically, it's the closest human equivalent to the enrichment conditions in mice that we discussed in the previous chapter! Cunning running therefore gets gold stars in relation to the *Three Keys*. Apparently, it can also become quite competitive and addictive, and you never know who you may meet along the way. Dr Kurrle:

> Orienteering is a brilliant activity for brain health because you're being physically active wandering from checkpoint to checkpoint, and mentally active working out the best route between checkpoints and trying not to get lost. It's great for all ages and activity levels. I clearly remember an older man trotting past me close to the finish of one event, only to discover that he was in the 90-plus age group! It's also great socially, because you sit down and discuss the best routes over a glass of wine after the competition.[4]

THINKING OUTSIDE THE BOX:
Real-world examples of keeping mentally fit

Men's Sheds
A quiet revolution is capturing the interest of many retired men out in the sleepy suburbs. Men's Sheds are places where men can go to learn and practise simple 'old school' skills such as carpentry, woodwork, metalwork and other handyman

tricks. There are now over 200 Men's Sheds around Australia. There is no code of practice covering these backyard activities, so the degree of competent supervision and safety issues need to be carefully assessed. Otherwise, they are an excellent way to challenge the mind by learning new skills, to socialise with other blokes and to get physical at the same time. Finding one in your local neighbourhood is now easy via the website <www.mensshed.org>

Shooting for the stars

Bert Bowden wrote to me about the sport of rifle shooting, which he has been passionately involved in for the past 35 years. He won a gold medal in the sport in the 1994 Commonwealth Games. The gold medallist at the 1982 Commonwealth Games, Arthur Clarke, was aged 62 at the time. Now in his eighties, he's still as bright as a button.

Competitive rifle shooting requires intense concentration, focus and calculation. According to Bert, there is always something new to learn. It is also very popular with the older age bracket—there are more keen shooters competing in the over sixties matches than in the open teams matches! Hence, competitive shooting nicely addresses all *Three Keys*: the cognitive, social and physical keys.

While only anecdotal, Bert makes the interesting comment that, of the thousands of members of rifle shooting clubs he has come into contact with across Australia and the world, none has retired from the sport through loss of mental abilities.

Outdoor adventure

John Flemming, aged 79 and from the North Island of New Zealand, loves to plan and undertake kayaking trips. He has done dozens of such trips, ranging in duration from a couple of days to a number of weeks. Mostly these trips comprise group paddles, but occasionally he sets himself a solo challenge, which requires him to travel alone for an extended period.

Like any serious outdoor adventure, a lot of precise and premeditated planning is required. Here is an example of some of the things John needs to consider when planning a trip:

The uppermost thing in my mind is the destination. Where and when? For how long? Solo or with company? What will I take? And, most important of all, what safety measures will apply?

Let's assume my destination will be Lake Taupo: a full circumnavigation (166 kilometres) will take three to four days. I'll check the weather forecast about a week before. If it looks good, I might decide to go solo. I'll need my comforts, so I'll pack a folding stretcher, chair and small table. A flysheet for cover, a sleeping mat and bag, and a bivvy sack will keep me warm and dry, and free of insects. If the nights are fine, I'll sleep out under the stars. If the conditions deteriorate, I'll camp-up and wait for an improvement.

I'll prepare two copies of a map of the lake by numbering off each kilometre and marking possible campsites. I'll take one copy with me and leave the other with a contact at home. I'll take my mobile phone (or a mountain radio if the reception is known to be bad) and a personal locator beacon. During the trip, I'll make nightly contact with home base and explain my plan for the following couple of days.

Before I leave I'll check my kayak, life jacket and other safety gear. I'll pack a spare paddle, cooking gear, an assortment of warm clothing including a windjacket, and medication including insect repellent. I'll carry a flask for hot soups or drinks. Ahead of the trip I'll prepare appetising and nutritious food for meals, and include sweets and fruit for nibbles.

> If I'm paddling solo, I'll always skirt close inshore in
> case of capsize, and I'll lay-up if the conditions are bad.[5]

Clearly, John is probably spending just as much *thinking* time as actual outdoors adventure time. Hence, the two keys of *mental activity* and *physical activity* are well and truly catered for. While solo adventure has its own special class of romantic and personal appeal, from a brain health point of view, group expeditions are the way to go in order also to unlock the *social activity* key to dementia prevention.

TEN FURTHER SUGGESTIONS

In no particular order, here are ten other activities to consider, each with a different mix of the *Three Keys*:

1. Volunteer with a community or charity group.
2. Learn a new language and travel with it.
3. Join a choir.
4. Take up drama classes or join an amateur theatre company.
5. Join a bushwalking and hiking club.
6. Join an interest group.
7. Start a local interest group.
8. Learn to paint, sculpt, write …
9. Learn how to use a computer and the internet.
10. Get a pet.

How much is enough?

Too much of anything can at some point become a negative. But how much is too much? Before tackling that question, there is an important point to make about the link between mental activities and risk for dementia, and that is the concept of a **dose-dependent effect**. What this means is that in many of the population studies referred to in Chapter 7, for each incremental step in participation in mental activities, there was a commensurate drop in risk for dementia. Let's take the example from the study mentioned earlier of 469 older individuals who initially didn't have dementia and whose fates were tracked for more than five years.[4] At the start of the study, all the participants completed a questionnaire on the frequency of participating in six different cognitive activities and were then placed into three categories: those with low levels, medium levels and high levels of activity. The rate of new dementia in the medium group compared to the low group was 50 per cent. The rate of new dementia in the high group compared to the low group was even lower—33 per cent.

Clearly, there is an advantage in keeping as active as possible, remembering to follow the principle of the *Three Keys*. However, if staying active starts to become a drain, stressful, or overly demanding, then this is counterproductive from a brain health perspective because, rather than protecting the brain, we may actually be doing it harm due to the build-up of the mild brain poison, cortisol. The best advice I can give is to *do as much as you can while keeping it fun* and therefore conserving your own equilibrium. We all need time to rest, relax and simply do nothing.

The question of 'how much am I doing now?' logically comes next. When reviewing this area during my studies for my PhD, I realised that there was no good tool or instrument available for comprehensively measuring people's mental activity levels across their life span. We therefore developed the *Lifetime of Experiences Questionnaire* (LEQ) to do just that. (See the *In Focus* section in this chapter.) The LEQ is available online. Within just 15 minutes, you can determine if your current levels of mental activity are in the low, medium or high range.

The Virtuous Cycle

The very simple message from these two 'use it or lose it' chapters is that, by employing the *Three Keys* and staying mentally, physically and socially active, we may decrease our chances of developing dementia, and so continue doing those things that bring meaning and happiness to our life. I like to call this the Virtuous Cycle, and it is captured in the following simple, but powerful, figure (see Figure 7).

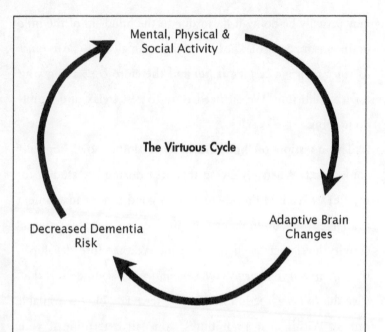

Figure 7 The Virtuous Cycle illustrates how following the *Three Keys* of mental, physical and social activity results in a range of beneficial brain changes, which in turn may reduce our risk for dementia, and so allow continued activity.

IN FOCUS Testing your mental activity levels

Many people want to know how their mental activity levels compare with those of their peers. The Lifetime of Experiences Questionnaire (LEQ) was designed for just this purpose and assesses the full range of complex mental pursuits that build up over a person's lifetime. It assumes that the respondent is over the age of 65 years or has already retired, and divides their experiences into the young adulthood, middle-age and late-life stages. Your educational, occupational, and complex mental and leisure pursuits are all assessed for each of these periods.

The LEQ produces an overall score, plus three sub-scores—one for young adulthood, one for middle age, and one for later life. There is obviously nothing you can do about your earlier life experiences (or sub-scores), but you can always increase your *current* range and intensity of mental pursuits and see how your later-life sub-score, and therefore overall score, improves.

The overall LEQ score is provided as a percentile—what percentage of the general population is below your score. So, if you score 50 per cent you are perfectly average, with 50 per cent below and 50 per cent above you; if you were to score 75 per cent, that means you are in the top 25 per cent; or a 90 per cent score would mean that only 10 per cent of your peers are scoring above you. Alternatively, a score of 20 per cent means that 80 per cent of individuals are working out their brains better than you are.

The general idea is that the higher the LEQ scores, the better. We have shown that higher LEQ scores not only predict a slower rate of cognitive change over time, but also a slower rate of brain shrinkage. As a general aspirational target,

I recommend that you aim to try to bring your overall LEQ score up above the 65 per cent range if possible.

To complete the LEQ, log into <train.headstrongcognitive.com/leq.aspx> and follow the prompts. It's free and will take about 15 minutes to complete. We record anonymous responses in order to build up a more accurate picture of what the 'typical' person's mental activity profile is like.

Finally, *remember that even a score of 99 per cent doesn't guarantee that you will avoid dementia.* What it *does* mean is that you are probably doing as much as humanly possible to reduce your chances of developing the condition.

CHAPTER 9

Exercising body and mind

Give a rat a running wheel and it will run its heart out — they love it. A young rat will run up to several kilometers per day of its own accord (actually mostly at night); even older animals will churn away. Yet when reports first emerged that running rodents developed better brain function, I was quite sceptical as to any potential importance to human health. After all, rodents naturally spend most of their time in highly active foraging for food and trying to avoid predators, and so it was not surprising that voluntary running had a big impact on the average lab rat's brain power, especially given that 'control' or comparison animals sit around doing nothing for their entire lives. Humans are different, right? It turns out I was wrong — utterly and gloriously wrong.

Human exercise trials

Over a dozen randomised clinical trials (**RCTs** — the highest level of medical evidence) have now investigated the impact of commencing physical exercise on cognitive function in later life — and the results are clear. Physical exercise does indeed have positive benefits on human mental function, especially the so-called 'executive' cognitive domains of problem solving and multi-tasking, as well as attention[1]. Furthermore, recent RCTs have shown that in those individuals with **Mild Cognitive Impairment** (**MCI**) — a preclinical condition of intermediate cognitive dysfunction that increases one's chances of developing dementia — exercise effectively reduces the rate of cognitive decline[2]. Physical exercise does therefore seem to have similar therapeutic effects in humans as it does in rodents.

When compared to the scientific studies of *mental* or *cognitive* exercise (as discussed in Chapter 7), several things stand out. First, the problematic issue of **transfer of effect**, which so bedevils the literature on mental exercise, does not apply to physical exercise. Clearly, walking, running or riding a bicycle does not involve the same mental processes as taking a memory test or solving a puzzle, and so there is no danger that positive cognitive effects from physical exercise are due to test practice. Because the nature of physical exercise is so different to cognitive task performance, there is an exemplary level of transfer of effect: one activity improves performance on another completely different type of activity. In my opinion, this is the biggest strength of the physical exercise field.

On the other hand, the **effect size** from studies of physical training appears to be smaller than those for cognitive training. Effect size in medical science refers to the magnitude or strength of a particular intervention on a particular outcome. Let's assume we are measuring pain (for example, due to headache) and we compare two interventions: one dose of paracetamol versus one dose of codeine. Both medicines are effective at lowering pain ratings, however if the number and type of patients in each group were to be well matched, the magnitude of pain relief for codeine would be greater; that is, its effect size would be greater. Another way of thinking about this is that the larger effect size for codeine means that you would need a smaller group of patients to demonstrate a statistically significant result. Listening to soothing music may be good for headache (or not), but its hypothetical effect size is so small you would need thousands of people in your experimental group to demonstrate its efficacy.

With this in mind, when it comes to cognitive function in older individuals, the effect size for physical exercise seems to be somewhat less than that for cognitive exercise. In a systematic review that I conducted with my colleague and mentor Professor Perminder Sachdev, we found that the effect size for cognitive training in healthy older adults was about 1.1 (a strong effect), while similar reviews for physical exercise have found effects size around 0.5-0.6 (a moderate effect). In the same review, we also found that this strong effect in favour of cognitive training lasted at least three months following the cessation of training, but few studies have looked at whether the beneficial effects of exercise continue after stopping. So even though cognitive training suffers (in a technical sense) from the challenge of adequately demonstrating transfer, it does seem to produce stronger benefits on mental function, and these may last longer after the end of any such training.

Of course, the best option may be to combine both physical and cognitive exercise. As explained when introducing *The Three Keys* principles in Chapter 8, rodent studies strongly indicate that the combination of mental exercise, physical activity and social engagement is much more powerful than either factor alone. Does the same apply to the human brain? At the moment we only have very tentative indications. In fact, a definitive answer may come from the SMART trial being conducted by Professor Maria Fiatarone Singh, of the University of Sydney, and various colleagues from around Australia including myself. In this RCT, older individuals at risk for dementia are randomly assigned to one of four conditions with different combination of physical and mental exercise. When complete (expected in late 2012), we will be able to calculate the effect size for cognitive training, physical exercise and the combination. We hypothesize that, as in animals, our participants will experience a greater benefit when undergoing combined physical-plus-mental exercise rather than either type of exercise by itself.

The big debate: Aerobic or resistance training?

One of the big unresolved questions in the physical exercise field is what type of training is best for the brain. A very basic type of categorization is between **aerobic exercise**, requiring sustained activity that raises your heart rate and metabolism (like jogging), or **resistance exercise**, where you maximally exert your muscles over a short intense period of time (like lifting weights).

This debate has a long history, first flaring up over the relative benefits of these exercise types on *somatic* (body) health. At first aerobic exercise was flavour of the month, driven by a stream of rodent studies which almost exclusively focused on the effect of running wheel use on physiology and disease processes (it being quite hard to get a mouse to lift weights!). Human studies of the impact of resistance training on somatic health then emerged, and for many years a vocal 'my type of exercise rules' mentality existed. Fortunately, a consensus has now emerged that, at least for general health, the combination of both aerobic and resistance training is optimal (somewhat unsurprisingly). For example, the HART-D trial in the United States compared the effect of aerobic, resistance and combined aerobic-plus-resistance training in diabetics to a sedentary control condition. In terms of reducing long-term blood sugar, only the combined type of physical exercise training was effective. Similar benefits of combined training have also been found for other general health conditions such as hypertension, osteoporosis and excess weight. For these reasons, the US American College of Sports Medicine and the American Heart Association recommend a combination of aerobic and resistance training for good general health. Now as we have seen in Chapters 3 to 6, all of these classic cardiovascular risk factors (especially hypertension) increase risk for dementia, and so any intervention that reduces cardiovascular disease will also be likely to (indirectly) reduce dementia risk. Therefore, for this reason alone, I recommend both aerobic and resistance exercise for optimal brain health. Yet it should be noted that, as yet, no RCTs have been carried out directly comparing aerobic, resistance or combined exercise training for the prevention of cognitive decline and dementia in older individuals.

What changes in the brain after physical exercise?

Amazingly, the simple act of engaging in physical exercise can lead to direct and measurable changes to our brain structure and function. At a basic level, any type of sustained physical exercise regime will improve your body's metabolic fitness — your heart will pump blood around more efficiently, your lungs will extract more oxygen from the air and release more CO_2, and so better enrich the blood. All cells in the body, including our brain cells, benefit from this fundamental adaptation. Since the brain demands the lion's share of body metabolism when the body is at rest, an overall increase in metabolic fitness is the first straightforward way that exercise could lead to better brain function. In fact, using brain imaging, it is possible to see the pattern of enhanced blood flow and metabolism in individuals after a period of physical exercise. Interestingly, recent studies suggest that physical exercise in older adults may specifically increase blood flow to the hippocampus, the brain structure intimately linked to memory and first affected in Alzheimer's disease.

Even more amazing (at least to me), are an increasing number of reports that physical exercise can increase the size of certain brain regions. Arthur Kramer and colleagues from the University of Illinois in the United States have led the field in this respect.

Using a whole-brain imaging technique, they first showed that healthy older individuals who were generally more active tended to have larger subparts of the prefrontal lobe (important for executive functions) and temporal lobe (important for memory). Furthermore, when scanned before and after six months of moderate-intensity aerobic exercise training, several brain regions were found to increase in volume when compared to a control group. In particular, volume of the anterior cingulate, a brain region in the frontal lobe important for proper attentional control of conflicting tasks, was increased. Most recently, this group has also shown that brisk walking over the course of a year was sufficient to increase the volume of the hippocampus, whilst the control group showed the expected volume decline[3]. In addition, in the exercise group, the degree of volume increase in the hippocampus was correlated to improvement in memory. This is therefore the best evidence to date that physical exercise can lead to mental benefits in older individuals by directly enhancing the structure and function of the hippocampus. What's more, on the basis of animal studies, we are starting to develop an increasingly sophisticated understanding of how exactly this may occur.

How does it work?

When the link between physical exercise and cognitive benefits first emerged, it was assumed to be purely a result of better general somatic health. Many argued it was simply due to better blood flow, metabolic fitness and reduced vascular disease. There is certainly an element of truth to this for, as mentioned earlier, physical exercise has powerful disease-busting effects on conditions such as diabetes, hypertension, excess weight and so on. When it comes to brain function, reducing or eliminating any of these vascular risk factors will lead to some form of benefit.

Yet studies of voluntary running in rodents soon established that exercise could also improve brain function directly through a variety of *central* mechanisms (the brain forms the Central Nervous System). For the sake of brevity, here we will focus on three most intriguing mechanisms, all related to new growth in the brain: neurogenesis (new brain cells), synaptogenesis (new connections between brain cells), and angiogenesis (new blood vessels).

As explained in previous chapters, neurogenesis is the most striking example of neuroplasticity because of the revolutionary discovery that new brain cells are continually being produced throughout adulthood. Environmental enrichment was found to be a strong driver for neurogenesis and, thereafter, researchers soon discovered that running alone was also a pro-neurogenesis stimulus. What's more, old rodents who ran were capable of boosting their neurogenesis levels up to that of young sedentary rodents after just a few months.

The new cells generated by neurogenesis in the hippocampus do not appear in any old place, rather in a specialised zone immediately adjacent to capillaries, the so-called *neurovascular niche*. Theo Palmer of the University of Stanford showed quite clearly that running not only produces new neurons, but also, through angiogenesis, new capillaries. This makes intuitive sense because if new brain cells are going to survive and contribute to a neuronal network, then these cells need nutrients via additional blood supply. What's more, researchers have shown in healthy older individuals that after a period of aerobic exercise training there is very specific increase in blood flow in this specialised subregion of the hippocampus, presumably because of increased angiogenesis.

Could then exercise-linked neurogenesis and angiogenesis account for the increase in hippocampal volume seen in humans after a year of training? While it's very hard to say, probably not by themselves, because by far and away the largest component of brain tissue volume is not the capillaries or the new neurons provided by neurogenesis, but rather the vast network of synaptic connections between brain cells. A couple of years ago my attention was therefore drawn to the possible link between synaptogenesis and exercise. Through the hard work of Joyce Siette, a PhD student supervised by Professor Fred Westbrook and me at the University of New South Wales, we have been able to make some interesting new insights into how exercise can produce unique effects on the older brain.

First, we needed to find a very sensitive rodent memory test in order to show that older rats were definitively impaired compared to young rats. We used a deceptively simple behavioural task. The place recognition memory (PRM) task requires a rat to go from its home cage to a new unfamiliar environment composed of two entirely novel objects (see Figure 8). The rat is allowed to explore for a few minutes then returns to its home cage for five minutes. During this delay, one of the objects is moved to a new position, and then the animal returns. Normally, a rat does what you would probably do if returning home to find your refrigerator in your bedroom — it has a good look at this strange object-in-a-new-position. This kind of preferential exploratory behaviour is quite convenient, in effect serving as a yardstick for rat memory. In other words, if the animal had no memory of the previous arrangement, it would not spend any extra time investigating the shifted object. The task has several advantages. Perhaps the most important is that by only a simple change in the process — rather than move an object around, we replace it with a new object — the task becomes a measure of object recognition memory (ORM). Importantly, for someone who is obsessed with the hippocampus (like me), PRM relies on intact hippocampal function, whilst ORM does not. So now we have two directly

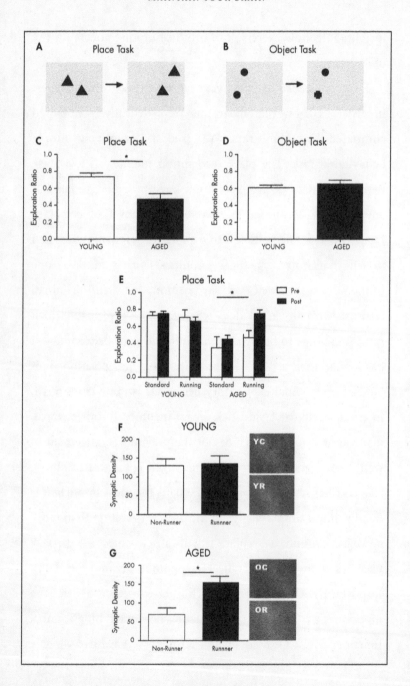

Figure 8 The effect of age and running on memory performance in rats.

A. This schematic shows the sequence and placement of objects in the rat's testing environment for the Place Recognition Memory test — a normal animal will preferentially explore the object whose position has moved. **B.** In the Object Recognition Memory test the position of objects are conserved, however one object has been replaced for a new object. **C.** Older animals are clearly impaired at the Place test, showing no preference for the new position (i.e., 0.5 or 50 per cent of time exploring one object compared to another). **D.** Older animals perform just as well as young animals on the Object test, suggesting that place memory impairment is specific in older rats. **E.** This graph shows place memory test performance in young and old rats before (pre) and after (post) a 12-week running or no-running interval. Running had no effect in younger animals. Older animals were initially impaired on place memory, and remained so under standard conditions. Running fully restored older animals' place memory abilities to that of younger animals. **F.** This graph shows synaptic density (connections between brain cells) in the hippocampus. Note that the normal synaptic density level in younger animals (approximately ~130) does not change after running. **G.** By contrast, sedentary older animals have much lower synaptic density (~65), which increases dramatically after a period of voluntary running (~155). Therefore older runners end up with more synaptic connections than even younger animals. The inserted pictures show examples of the actual synaptic connections under the microscope — low synaptic density appears as patches of dark image intensity, while high density appear as lighter image intensity. **Note: A solid line with asterisk denotes a statistically significant difference.** *All images courtesy of Joyce Siette, University of New South Wales.*

comparable tasks of distinct memory systems — made by only the most minor changes in stimuli — which can give us an insight on two different aspects of brain function. Perfect.

As shown in Figure 8, we then used these behavioural tools to show that while ageing clearly impairs the rodent's place recognition memory system, it has no effect on object recognition. Next, we tested the impact of three months' voluntary running in both younger and older rats. This type of exercise returned older animals' place recognition memory back to the levels of young animals. We then looked at what was happening in the hippocampus and discovered some very interesting effects. As we knew from prior research, we found that age had a negative impact on neurogenesis and, furthermore, that neurogenesis was increased by about 50 per cent in runners, irrespective of age. So in other words, old runners had their neurogenesis levels restored to levels of sedentary youngsters, but were still far below young runners. But against conventional wisdom, we also found that there was no correlation between neurogenesis levels and place memory. So, while running is quite effective at increasing the production of new brain cells at any age, it does not seem to be linked to an animal's ability to remember the position of objects in the environment.

Quite a different pattern was found for synapses. Figure 8 shows that the pattern of synaptic changes following exercise resembled that for place recognition memory: synaptic numbers did not change in younger animals, but increased dramatically (by more than 150 per cent) in older animals. In fact, for the first time, we showed that running could increase synapses in the old hippocampus to levels in excess of younger animals. What's more, in some parts of the hippocampus, synaptic number were extremely highly correlated with place recognition memory performance, indicating that it is the density of connections between brain cells in the hippocampus, rather brain cell numbers *per se*, which is vital for short term memory for places.

How does running increase synaptic connections in the hippocampus? At least in rats, the answer appears to be quite interesting and unexpected. Professor György Buzsáki of Rutgers University in New Jersey carried out the following most remarkable experiment: He had mice run in a wheel, perform a maze in which they were rewarded for alternately taking right or left turns, come back to the wheel and run some more, return to the maze, and so forth. The mice had electrodes implanted into their hippocampus so the investigators could record in real time the firing pattern of individual brain cells during the whole process. They found that when mice ran in the wheel they were 'rehearsing' the neural firing sequences they had learnt during the maze. Not only were they rehearsing, they appeared to be 'thinking about' what navigation decision they were about to make. Incredibly, computer analysis of hippocampal firing patterns during wheel running could predict, quite accurately, whether the animal was going to make a left or right turn in the following maze circuit, even when animals got mixed up and made the wrong turn! So at least in rodents, running seems to be intimately linked with cognitive processing, helping to rehearse and predict life-changing patterns in their external environment.

Does the same apply to the human brain? Here we really have almost no data to say. Without question, the hippocampus is vital to human memory formation, but in relative volume terms it has shrunk from about 3.5 per cent of brain space in rodents to less than 0.5 per cent in humans. We do a lot more with our brains than simply run, forage, eat and sleep, as rodents do, and so the role of the hippocampus has evolved. One interesting theory is that during sleep, memories are consolidated from short-term memory (which is highly *hippocampal*) to long-term memory (which is thought to be distributed widely throughout our cortex). Thus with more exercise, we certainly sleep better, and this may help better memory consolidation[4]. I do love walking to work every day and seem to sort out a lot of things in my head along the way. It is quite possible that exercise and cognitive processing are linked in humans as it is in rodents.

In recent years, we have also learnt a great deal about the role of central and **somatic growth factors**, molecules directly activated by exercise (mental or physical) and which trigger the cellular growth processes mentioned above. Professor Carl Cotman from University of California, Irvine USA, is a world leader in this field[5]. He has confirmed the importance of activation of brain-derived neurotrophic growth factor (BDNF) to setting off molecular cascades that end up with increased neurogenesis, synaptogenesis and angiogenesis. For example, if one blocks BDNF production, then these growth processes are not properly activated following running, and animals do not seem to benefit mentally. BDNF production takes about three days of physical exercise to increase, stays high during exercise, and then starts to wane after about two weeks following cessation. In terms of brain health, physical exercise may therefore have a short-lived effect after training is stopped, but a lot more research is required to answer this important question.

Interestingly, BDNF and several other growth factors and related molecules also increase following exercise in the general blood circulation. BDNF cannot cross the **blood-brain barrier** (**BBB**), so why this happens is not clear. It may, for example, help trigger muscle growth outside the brain; or there may be a molecule (as yet not found) that passes the BDNF signal from outside the BBB to BDNF inside the brain — neither of these ideas is proven. However, other growth factors do cross the BBB, and so there is increasing awareness that exercise-induced changes in somatic factors could end up influencing brain health. For example, vascular endothelial growth factor (VEGF) is stimulated in the blood vessels and helps stimulate angiogenesis in the body, so that blood supply can keep up with muscle growth. Yet VEGF also crosses the BBB and helps stimulate angiogenesis and neurogenesis, in effect 'feeding' the neurovascular niche where neurogenesis occurs.

Another important example of a somatic factor that may link general health and brain health is insulin growth factor (IGF-1). Exercise produces a strong positive effect on IGF-1 in the blood circulation, which in turn helps lower blood sugar and prevent the development of diabetes. In addition, IGF-1 crosses the BBB and so may be a mechanism by which exercise protects the brain from the harmful effects of excess blood sugar (as discussed in Chapter 4). By contrast, exercise reduces many inflammatory cytokines (another class of somatic factor), a change which also helps prevent the development of inflammatory diseases as diverse as arthritis, atherosclerosis (heart disease) and again diabetes. Some of these inflammatory factors can also cross the BBB, and so their reduction following exercise may help protect the brain from inflammatory damage.

It therefore appears that physical exercise can lead to positive brain changes through a number of different biological pathways. Some of these are central — within and unique to the brain — while others are somatic, in which physiological adaptations that benefit general body health may transfer to the brain. The relative importance of central versus somatic mechanisms is difficult to say, and like most dichotomies applied to the brain, probably a false one. Professor Cotman sums it up nicely:

> For a long time exercise was thought to act exclusively on body fitness by strengthening muscles, improving cardiovascular fitness and overall circulation. In the mid 90s this assumption began to be challenged. Exercise is now known to produce many, many effects on the brain, including increasing synapses, enhancing neurogenesis, and building the vascular system. Exercise also improves learning, relieves stress and can counteract depression. However, exercise also regulates body-wide functions. In a sense we have come full circle. Exercise works in a coordinated manner, both peripherally and centrally, to build body and brain health. Each is essential and the total is greater than the sum of its parts. From my perspective this mechanism is brilliant in its totality. It is one of the best examples of a mind body connection.

A conceptual model

A simplified understanding of how exercise may positively influence brain health is provided in Figure 9. Both the somatic and central pathways are important, with many somatic factors able to cross the blood-brain-barrier to positively influence brain structure and function.

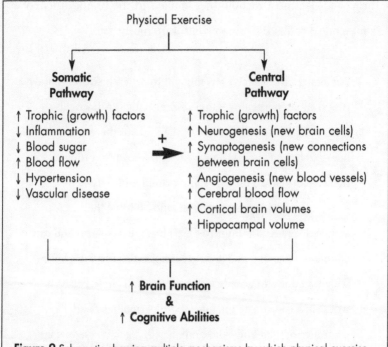

Figure 9 Schematic showing multiple mechanisms by which physical exercise can improve brain health and function.

The idea that somatic factors can change brain performance is of considerable interest to the pharmaceutical industry, with the development of exercise-in-a-pill a holy grail of sorts. One group in the United States (including Australian Dr Michael Downes) generated a lot of excitement by studying a particular class of somatic factors generated in the muscle of exercising rodents. These molecules are important for regulating metabolism in all cells, and when animals are genetically modified to over-produce this compound they end up leaner (without exercise), and when given the chance to run become 'super-runners', able to outrun a normal mouse by 100 per cent! When normal mice are fed a compound based on these molecules they also increase their lean muscle bulk and running endurance[6]. In addition, another group reported in 2011 that giving mice this same drug also appears to help brain function on some memory tests (but not others), and increases hippocampal neurogenesis. Importantly, neither of these effects was as strong as stimulated by regular exercise. Furthermore, these metabolic drugs have many side effects and so there is a lot more research to go before anything like this reaches human trials, or let alone your local pharmacy. Personally, I doubt a drug will ever be able to fully mimic the marvellously multifaceted positive effects that physical exercise has not only on general body health but also brain health.

Conclusions

Clinical research and a lot of good basic science suggest that physical exercise is effective for promoting brain health. It is also highly likely that exercise is effective for minimising cognitive decline in older individuals. For these reasons, physical activity represents the *Third Key* in the *The Three Keys* to helping prevent dementia.

Lesson #6: *Physical exercise is linked to brain health, and increasing regular physical exercise levels most likely helps maintain cognitive function.*

Recommendation #6: *Incorporate physical activity and exercise into your day-to-day lifestyle.*

So how much exercise should you be doing? When it comes to brain health, we still do not fully understand how much and what type of exercise is best. What is clear, however, is that even a relatively modest increase in physical exercise, like walking vigorously three times a week for 45 minutes, can be useful. The previous chapter has several examples of activities which not only represent good physical exercise, but are also mentally and socially engaging — the ideal mix of *The Three Keys'* ingredients.

When it comes to general physical health, the American College of Sports Medicine and the America Heart Association recommend the following combinations of aerobic and resistance training exercise:

Individuals aged less than 65 years should do 30 minutes of moderate exercise at least five times a week. Moderate exercise means at least a brisk walk. In addition, at least 20 minutes a week should be devoted to resistance exercises such as weights, push-ups or sit-ups.

For those aged 65 years or older, 30 minutes of exercise three to four times a week is recommended. Moderate exercise in this case is anything that feels not too strenuous, not too light. In addition, strengthening exercises for the main muscle groups are recommended on two non-consecutive days of the week. Regular stretching and balance exercises are also suggested for the prevention of falls.

CHAPTER 10

Bringing it together

Recommendation 1: Heart health means brain health—Maintain a healthy blood pressure

Dementia remains an enigma, not only to the patients themselves but also to their families, carers, treating doctors, and the scientists struggling to find new treatments. The neural mechanisms that sustain the core cognitive functions that are so relevant to dementia—memory, attention, inhibition, personality— remain deeply mysterious. Furthermore, for over 100 years we scientists have been viewing dementia through a pair of classical spectacles that have focused almost exclusively on the presence or absence of clumps of protein, the amyloid plaques mentioned throughout this book. It is perhaps only in the last few years that researchers have started to appreciate the normal physiological roles of these much-maligned proteins, and so a silent disquiet with the classical amyloid hypothesis is becoming more vocal and more confident.

I suspect that it is only through further counter-orthodox and creative thinking that truly revolutionary new treatments for Alzheimer's Dementia will begin to emerge.

Part of this new thinking has been an appreciation of the close connection between Vascular Dementia and Alzheimer's Dementia. In population-based research, almost every vascular risk factor—hypertension, smoking, obesity, diabetes, high cholesterol—has been linked to increased risk for *both* VaD *and* AD. At a more fundamental biological level, there is a growing list of experimental studies showing how, by simply changing vascular factors such as local blood supply, we can change the pattern of development of AD pathology in genetically modified animals. And there are now new hypotheses emerging that directly link the development of AD pathology with subtle weak points in the brain's vascular architecture.

The good news is that such an open-minded attitude has led to one great success story in the prevention of dementia. The only medical therapy with a proven effect on the development of dementia is the treatment of hypertension. So, *the number one best thing that a person can do to prevent dementia is maintain a healthy blood pressure.* As mentioned elsewhere, when it comes to dementia, ensure maintaining a healthy blood pressure becomes an almost religious belief.

Yet, hypertension goes untreated in large swathes of the older population. This must be viewed as unacceptable to a society evidently worried about dementia. In fact, a recent survey found that nearly 80 per cent of Australians were not aware of the link between high blood pressure and dementia. Clearly, a new awareness campaign is required to educate both laypeople and GPs about the benefits to the brain of normalising hypertension.

Fortunately, this part of the dementia prevention message can 'piggyback' on the fantastic levels of health knowledge that currently exist about cardiovascular disease. We all know what to do to keep our heart healthy: avoid smoking, take regular exercise, eat balanced meals, avoid excess weight, and so forth. So, the dementia prevention message fits nicely with the cardiac disease prevention message: when it comes to dementia, what is good for the heart is good for the brain.

Clearly, what is now required is conversion of this awareness into action, since Australians just keep getting more overweight. A continuation of the status quo will lead not only to a greater burden of chronic heart disease, but also to an increase in dementia rates for every age bracket.

Recommendation 2: Exercise your brain as well as your muscles

Given that what's good for the heart is good for the brain, it seems the reverse analogy works equally well. Physical exercise keeps our muscles, especially our heart muscles, strong and resilient; similarly, mental exercise is important for keeping our brain strong and resilient.

The links between mental activity and reduced dementia risk are now hard to deny. The strongest evidence comes from a range of clinical trials that have found that cognitive exercise of one form or another slows the rate of cognitive decline in older individuals. Clinical trials are also starting to show that mental activity of this sort transfers to measures of general cognition and everyday function. To this we can add strong links between mental activity and lower dementia rates in population studies, as well as a host of beneficial brain changes. Hence, the likelihood that a similar strategy may work for the prevention of dementia is extremely high. Accordingly, clinical trials with dementia incidence as outcome measures are currently under way around the world.

There is also good evidence that combining cognitive training with a social dimension and physical exercise may well be better than cognitive exercise alone.

Recommendation 3: Make physical exercise a part of everyday life

For a long time it was thought that physical exercise helped improve brain fitness simply through its general disease-busting effects. Now it is clear that physical exercise stimulates a number of positive growth processes in the brain, including neurogenesis (new brain cells), angiogenesis (new blood vessels), and most importantly, synaptogenesis (new brain connections). Furthermore, many human clinical trials have shown that exercise leads to better cognitive function, especially in older persons. Physical activity should therefore be incorporated into one's lifestyle, and include elements of both aerobic and resistance exercise.

Recommendation 4: Choose activities that satisfy the *Three Keys* principle

The *Three Keys* principle means deliberately incorporating leisure and pastime activities with a cognitive, social and physical component into your lifestyle, particularly after retirement. There are an almost limitless number and diversity of activities that handsomely satisfy the *Three Keys* principle, and we have covered a few of these in some detail. Importantly, in order to follow this principle for the rest of your life, and so get maximum protection from dementia, you need to find these activities fun and rewarding.

Hence, maintaining a diverse range of cognitive, social and physical activities is essentially about *quality of life*. It is no coincidence that, time and time again, 'what people rate as essential for *happiness* includes having good relationships, a satisfying and challenging job, and the ability to get out and enjoy nature and the environment. So, prevention of dementia equates to maximising happiness and quality of life. This seems like a beautiful equation.

Of course, by integrating the *Three Keys* into our lifestyle, our cardiovascular fitness will improve and so minimise the risk of hypertension, which further lowers our risk for dementia and allows us to continue participating in these activities that bring us meaning and pleasure. If there is one central message from this book, I hope it is a resounding call to begin to cultivate this virtuous cycle. This principle not only treats mind and body as one, but also acknowledges the unity of the brain and heart.

Recommendation 5: All bets are off—do the best you can

When it comes to dementia, as in life, there are no guarantees. Whether because of inherited genes or the effects of a complex biological process that we don't yet fully understand, some individuals who follow all the best advice will still develop dementia.

We can, however, *minimise* our risk for dementia. We can also *delay* its appearance should we have strong underlying risks. Like all good risk management advice, there are rarely 100 per cent guarantees against bad outcomes; instead, there are only preventative strategies aimed at reducing such risks to the best of our abilities. For the moment, dementia risk lies in precisely this bracket.

The aim of this book has therefore been to distil and evaluate the hundreds of research studies, articles and often-contradictory findings about dementia, in order to best equip the reader for managing their risk for the condition. As we have seen, there have been blind alleys, unexpected twists and turns, some disappointments, but also some good news.

Perhaps the best of the good news is that one's risk for dementia isn't fixed. By attending to our cardiovascular and brain health, we can in all likelihood reduce our risk for dementia. Even better, it seems we can reap these benefits even if we commence these lifestyle changes later in life. In which case, it truly does appear that *it's never too late to change your mind!*

IN FOCUS Summary

Top 5 things you can do to avoid dementia

Here is a summary of what we have covered about how best to avoid dementia. Strategies with the strongest available evidence appear at the top of the list. Remember, there are no guarantees; just the individual challenge to minimise your personal risk.

1. Strive for a healthy blood pressure

Lowering blood pressure from high to normal is the only pharmacological treatment proven to reduce the incidence of dementia. Apart from that, there are a number of links between good cardiac health and good brain health. Remember the simple equation: Strong Heart = Strong Brain. See Chapter 3 for more information.

Get your blood pressure checked by a GP, and discuss the full range of non-pharmacological and pharmacological options if it is high. If it is only slightly elevated, then physical exercise is the best way to bring it down naturally!

2. The *Three Keys*: Mental, Physical and Social activity

Basic animal research, long-term human studies and emerging clinical trials all point to the brain benefits of mental and physical exercise, particularly in later life. The social dimension is also important, as it forces us to use our brain in a different way. Individuals who practise a mental task with other people obtain greater benefits than those who practise it alone. See Chapters 7 to 9 for more information.

Start a new pastime, hobby or leisure activity that stimulates your brain and body, and includes other people!

3. Eat oily fish

Eating oily fish definitely improves our cardiac health, and so is likely to improve brain health. Trials are under way to test whether the likely active ingredient, Omega 3 oils, can reduce dementia risk. See Chapter 4 for more information.

Include oily fish in your diet 2–3 times a week!

4. Drink the Mediterranean way

If you drink alcohol, then avoid binge drinking altogether. There may, however, be minor benefits from having alcohol in modest, regular amounts. If you don't drink at all, there is no compelling evidence that you should start to drink alcohol to help prevent dementia. See Chapter 4 for more information.

If you drink alcohol, include a glass or two of wine with your meal a few times a week!

5. Eat a balanced diet high in natural antioxidants

There is no clear evidence that eating any particular food (besides fish) can specifically reduce our dementia risk. However, a balanced diet high in natural antioxidants will definitely help maintain good general health. A Western diet of highly processed and convenience foods can risk the development of obesity and diabetes, and there is increasing evidence linking these with dementia. See Chapter 4 for more information.

Aim for a healthy weight by eating a balanced diet high in natural antioxidants and that matches your daily energy needs!

Endnotes

Chapter 1 — What is dementia?

1 Professor Anthony Jorm, Department of Psychiatry, University of Melbourne. Conversation with the author, 23 October 2006.

2 Access Economics, *The Dementia Epidemic: Economic impact and positive solutions for Australia*, Canberra, 2003.

Chapter 2 — The main forms of dementia

1 Translation by Manuel B. Graeber, *Brain Pathology*, 1999, 9:237–40.

2 MRC CFAS. Pathological correlates of late-onset dementia in a multicentre, community-based population in England and Wales. *Lancet* (2001) 375:169–75.

3 P.S. Sachdev, H. Brodaty, M.J. Valenzuela, L. Lorentz, J.C. Looi, W. Wen and A.S. Zagami, 'The neuropsychological profile of vascular cognitive impairment in stroke and TIA patients', *Neurology*, 23 March 2004, 62(b): 912–9.

Chapter 3 — A healthy heart means a healthy brain

1 K.J. Anstey et al, 'Smoking as a risk factor for dementia and cognitive decline: a meta-analysis of prospective studies', *American Journal of Epidemiology*, 2007, 166(4):367–78.

2 K. Langa, N. Forster and E. Larson, 'Mixed dementia: emerging concepts and therapeutic implications', *JAMA*, 2004, 292:2901–8.

3   Associate Professor Dr Karen Cullen, University of Sydney. Conversation with author, 22 May 2008.
4   O. Hanon and F. Forette, 'Treatment of hypertension and prevention of dementia', *Alzheimer's & Dementia*, 2005, 1:30–37.
5   D.M. Lloyd-Jones, J.C. Evans and D. Levy, 'Hypertension in adults across the age spectrum: current outcomes and control in the community', *JAMA*, 2005, 294:466–72.

Chapter 4 — Food for thought
1   D. Ames and C. Ritchie, 'Antioxidants and Alzheimer's disease: time to stop feeding vitamin E to dementia patients,' *International Psychogeriatrics*, 2007, 19:1–8.
2   M. Mazza, A. Capuano, P. Bria and S. Mazza, 'Ginkgo biloba and donepezil: a comparison in the treatment of Alzheimer's dementia in a randomized placebo-controlled double-blind study,' *European Journal of Neurology*, 2006, 13:981–5.
3   H. Dodge, et al., 'A randomized placebo-controlled trial of ginkgo biloba for the prevention of cognitive decline', *Neurology*, 2008, e-published ahead of print.
4   Press release 'Does Gingko Biloba Affect Memory', 27 February 2008, American Academy of Neurology.
5   Y. Freund-Levi, M. Eriksdotter-Jonhagen, T. Cederholm, H. Basun, G. Faxen-Irving, A. Garlind, I. Vedin, B. Vessby, L.O. Wahlund and J. Palmblad, 'Omega-3 fatty acid treatment in 174 patients with mild to moderate Alzheimer disease: OmegAD study: a randomized double-blind trial,' *Arch Neurol*, October 2006, 63(10):1402–8.
6   American Heart Association, *Fish Consumption, Fish Oil, Omega-3 Fatty Acids and Cardiovascular Disease*, November 2002.
7   G. Biessels, S. Staekenborg, E. Brunner, C. Brayne and P. Scheltens, 'Risk of dementia in diabetes mellitus: a systematic review', *Lancet Neurology*, 2006, 5:64–74.

Chapter 5 — What's the story with cholesterol?
1   B. Wolozin, 'Cholesterol and the biology of Alzheimer's disease', *Neuron*, 2004, 41:7–10.

2   L. Shobab, G. Hsiung and H. Feldman, 'Cholesterol in Alzheimer's disease', *Lancet Neurology*, 2005, 4:841–52.

3   L.R. Drew and A.S. Truswell, 'Wernicke's encephalopathy and thiamine fortification of food: time for a new direction?', *The Medical Journal of Australia*, 1998, 168:534–5.

Chapter 6 — Homocysteine: The new cholesterol?

1   C. Boushey, S. Beresford, G. Omenn and A. Motulsky, 'A quantitative assessment of plasma homocysteine as a risk factor for vascular disease: probable benefits of increasing folic acid intakes', *JAMA*, 1995, 274:1049–57.

2   A.G. Bostom et al., 'Nonfasting plasma total homocysteine levels and stroke incidence in elderly persons: the Framingham Study', *Annals of Internal Medicine*, 1999, 131:352–5.

3   P. Sachdev, 'Homocysteine and brain atrophy', *Progress in Neuropsychopharmacology & Biological Psychiatry*, 2005, 29:1152–61.

4   M. Savaria Morris, 'Homocysteine and Alzheimer's disease', *Lancet Neurology*, 2003, 2:425–8.

5   M. Ellinson, J. Thomas and A. Patterson, 'A critical evaluation of the relationship between serum vitamin B12, folate and total homocysteine with cognitive impairment in the elderly', *Journal of Human Nutrition and Dietetics*, 2004, 17:371–83.

6   L. Bazzano, K. Reynolds, K. Holder and J. He, 'Effects of folic acid supplementation on risk of cardiovascular diseases: a meta-analysis of randomised controlled trials', *JAMA*, 2006, 296:2720–6.

7   M. Malouf, et al., 'Folate with or without vitamin B12 for cognition and dementia, *Cochrane Review, The Cochrane Library*, Issue 4, John Wiley & Sons, Chichester, UK.

8   Sachdev, P. Homocysteine and Alzheimer disease: an intervention study. Nature Reviews Neurology. 2011, 7: 9-10

Chapter 7 — Use it or lose it — Part 1: The science

1   M. Valenzuela, M. Breakspear and P. Sachdev, 'Complex mental activity: molecular, cellular and cortical network mechanisms', *Brain Research Reviews*, 2007, 56:198–213.

2   M. Valenzuela, et al., 'Neural stem cells for neuropsychiatric disorders', *Acta Neuropsychiatrica*, 2007, 19:11–26.

3   Associate Professor Kuldip Sidhu, Faculty of Medicine, University of New South Wales. Conversation with author, 11 February 2008.

4   G. Kempermann, *Adult Neurogenesis*, Oxford University Press, 2006.

5   M. Valenzuela and P. Sachdev, 'Can cognitive exercise prevent the onset of dementia? A systematic review of randomized clinical trials with longitudinal follow up', *American Journal of Geriatric Psychiatry*, 2008, in press.

6   S.L. Willis et al., 'Long-term effects of cognitive training on everyday functional outcomes in older adults', *JAMA*, 2006, 296:2805–14.

7   G.W. Rebok et al., 'Training and maintaining memory abilities in healthy older adults: traditional and novel approaches', *Journals of Gerontology: SERIES B*, 2007, 62B:53–61.

Chapter 8 — Use it or lose it — Part 2: The art

1   J.R. Cracchiolo et al., 'Enhanced cognitive activity—over and above social or physical activity—is required to protect Alzheimer's mice against cognitive impairment, reduce A, deposition, and increase synaptic immunoreactivity', *Neurobiology of Learning and Memory*, 2007, 88:277–94.

2   J. Verghese et al., 'Leisure activities and the risk of dementia in the elderly', *New England Journal of Medicine*.

3   Bruce Lee, *The Tao of Jeet Kune Do*, Ohara Publications Inc., 1975.

4   Associate Professor Sue Kurrie, Hornsby Hospital, Sydney. Conversation with author, 11 May 2008.

Chapter 9 — Exercising Body and Mind

1   C. Hillman, K. Erickson, and A. Kramer, 'Be smart, exercise your heart: Exercise effects on brain and cognition', *Nature Reviews Neuroscience* 9, pp. 58–65, 2008.

2   N. Lautenschlager. et al., 'Effect of physical activity on cognitive function in older adults at risk for Alzheimer Disease', *Journal of the American Medical Association*, 300, pp. 1027–1037, 2008.

3 K. I. Erickson et al., 'Exercise training increases size of hippocampus and improves memory', *Proceedings of the National Academy of Sciences USA*, 108, pp. 3017–3022, 2011.

4 R. Stickgold, 'Sleep-dependent memory consolidation', *Nature*, 437, pp. 1272–1278, 2005.

5 C. Cotman, N. Berchtold and L. Christie, 'Exercise builds brain health: Key roles of growth factor cascades and inflammation', *Trends in Neuroscience*, 30, pp. 464–471, 2007.

6 V. Narkar et al., 'AMPK and PPARδ agonists are exercise mimetics', *Cell*, 134, pp. 405–415, 2008.

Online resources

www.alzheimers.org.au
Website of the Alzheimer's Australia organisation with links about dementia, as well as information for individuals with the disease, family and carers, healthcare professionals and researchers.

www.alzheimers.org.au/upload/MYM_book_lowres.pdf
Mind Your Mind dementia prevention campaign booklet by Alzheimer's Australia.

www.brainage.med.unsw.edu.au
Brain & Ageing Program of the University of New South Wales, of which the author is part. Provides information on the diverse range of research projects currently under way at UNSW related to ageing and dementia.

www.alzforum.com

A US-based network of Alzheimer researchers. Covers the latest research findings, and includes a database of clinical trials and profiles of investigators.

www.alz.co.uk/adi/wad

Basic information from the UK Alzheimer's Society about World Alzheimer's Day (21 September in 2008) and Alzheimer's Disease International. Also information about Vascular Dementia, which is very common but receives less attention than AD dementia.

Glossary

The number after an entry refers to the page where the term appears in bold on first usage.

A

Aerobic exercise, 162

A type of physical exercise which involves continuous activity over at least 10 minutes and increases heart rate and respiratory rate.

Alzheimer's Disease (AD), 18

Clinical AD (or AD dementia) refers to a progressive brain disease that typically begins after age 60 and is distinct from normal ageing. Generally starts with an *amnestic syndrome* which deteriorates to include impairments in most *cognitive domains* and loss of day-to-day function (i.e., *dementia*). *Pathological* AD refers to a high concentration of beta-amyloid plaques and neurofibrillary tangles when brains of older individuals are seen under the microscope. Not all clinical AD patients have pathological AD when examined after death, and not all pathological AD cases had clinical AD in life. Coexistence of both AD dementia and Vascular Dementia in the same individual is increasingly recognised.

Amnestic syndrome, 30
Consistent problems with memory beyond those generally seen for someone of that age.

Amyloid hypothesis, 33
A classical hypothesis for the development of AD in which abnormal clumps of the beta-amyloid protein are deposited as plaques in the extracellular brain space, causing loss of neurons and synapses and preceding the development of memory problems.

Antioxidants, 73
Biological compounds which counteract and neutralise the toxic effects of oxidants.

APOE gene, 119
Part of the genetic code (DNA) on chromosome 19 which codes for the production of apolipoprotein E. Humans exhibit one of

four variations in this gene: APOE2,2, APOE2,3, APOE 3,4 and APOE4,4. Carriage of the APOE4 variant, while not as common as 2 and 3, increases the chances of developing AD dementia.

Apolipoprotein E, 112

A highly specialised type of protein for transporting cholesterol from astrocytes and into the neuron.

Astrocytes, 112

The most common type of cell in the brain, outnumbering neurons by more than 10:1. They have a number of important functions, including providing nutrients to the neuron from the microvasculature, and eliminating and recycling waste products.

Attention, 22

A cognitive domain referring to our ability to focus concentration on a particular task at hand, or to split our concentration between two or more tasks at the same time.

Axons, 43

The elongated extensions of individual neurons which link them together. Millions of axons together make up the *white matter* of the brain by virtue of their fatty myelin sheathing which serves as insulation, and also makes them appear pale to the naked eye compared to the unmyelinated *grey matter*.

B

Beta-amyloid, 33

A type of protein that is naturally generated by cleavage of the Amyloid Precursor Protein (APP), which spans across the neuronal outer cell membrane, particularly in the synaptic zone of the neuron. Neuronal activity increases production of beta-amyloid, which may serve a physiological function by in turn reducing synaptic activity through negative feedback. High levels of beta-amyloid (for whatever reason) lead to its deposition as *amyloid plaques* in the extracellular space between neurons—which, according to the classical hypothesis for AD, is neurotoxic and the starting point for the disease.

Blood-brain barrier (BBB), 211

The blood-brain barrier (BBB) refers to the very tight junction between cells which make up the blood vessels of the brain, so that only very small molecules can pass from the blood directly into the brain.

C

Calcium channel blockers, 63

A class of anti-hypertensive medicines that were found to prevent development of dementia in older hypertensive adults in one study.

Cerebral infarction, 52

Synonymous with stroke; a sudden reduction in blood supply to a part of the brain, leading to dysfunction and death of brain cells.

Cerebrovascular disease, 43

A broad term covering a range of potential pathologies to the blood supply of the brain, including *macrovascular disease* such as strokes caused by blockage or haemorrhage of major blood vessels, and *microvasculature disease* which includes damage to the fine capillaries that transfer nutrients to the brain cells.

Cerebrovasculature, 50

The system of blood vessels that supply the brain. Arteries, arterioles and capillaries supply nutrient-rich blood (in descending order of magnitude), and venules and veins drain nutrient-depleted blood back to the heart.

Cholesterol, 52

A fat-based biological compound. Outside the brain, it is derived from our diet and is highly regulated by the liver, while within the brain it is manufactured by astrocytes. LDL cholesterol is a major transportable form of cholesterol which enters and is stored by body cells; HDL cholesterol is the main form for eliminating it from cells. Cholesterol is a vital ingredient in the outer cell membrane of all cells, particularly *neurons.*

Cholesterol lipid rafts, 112

Cholesterol is integrated into a *neuron's* outer cell membrane as floating 'rafts' or platforms. Cholesterol rafts are critical for a range of neural functions, including *synaptic transmission.*

Cognitive domains, 21

A system of classifying higher brain function into broad groups of skills and abilities that are important for human day-to-day function: e.g., memory, attention, problem solving, inhibition.

Correlation, 37

A linear relationship between two variables, so that a fixed increment in one leads to a predictable increment in the other.

Cortisol, 153

A hormone secreted by the adrenal gland into the circulation in times of stress. Its normal physiological purpose is as an anti-inflammatory; however, it is particularly toxic to sensitive neurons in the hippocampus.

D

Dementia, 17

An irreversible clinical syndrome of progressive loss of cognitive functions that typically begins with memory problems, and then worsens to affect basic day-to-day function and activities. Often begins in late life (aka sporadic dementia), but not always as evident as younger onset dementia. The two main pathological processes linked to dementia are Alzheimer's Disease and cerebrovascular disease.

Dose-dependent effect, 241

A particularly strong type of research finding in which an intervention or risk factor is not just *associated with* a significant outcome; every stepwise increase in the intervention 'dose' or level of a risk factor *predicts* a commensurate stepwise increase or decrease in the outcome. Closely related to the concept of *correlation*.

E

Effect size, 197

A statistical measure of the strength of particular intervention in comparison to a control group. Stronger effect sizes mean that smaller groups of patients are needed to demonstrate a statistically significant result and vice versa.

Environmental enrichment, 151

An experimental manipulation from the rodent field in which animals are moved from standard housing to cages with more space and cohabitants, more toys and mazes for exploration, and running wheels for exercise. A general finding over decades of research is that enrichment improves animals' cognitive and motor function, as well as enhancing a range of brain variables.

Extracellular space, 33

In the brain, this refers to the space *between neurons* and *astrocytes* which is filled with fluid that eventually drains into the *ventricles*.

F

Folate, 129

A vitamin found in green leafy vegetables that is critical for proper neural development in the womb, and in adulthood is required for the production of methionine, an amino acid. Increased oral folate is an effective treatment of raised homocysteine.

G

Gamma-secretase, 113

One of a number of key enzymes in the generation of beta-amyloid. Gamma-secretase is embedded into the outer cell membrane of all neurons, particularly in the synaptic area.

Grey matter, 237

Brain tissue composed of the cell bodies of neurons. Because this part of the neuron is non-myelinated, it appears darker to the naked eye than myelinated white matter.

H

High-density lipoproteins (HDLS) *see* **Cholesterol**, 109

Hippocampus, 35

A pair of folded-up, sausage-shaped structures (*hippocampus* meaning *seahorse* in Greek) deep in the base of the brain which is critical to memory function (especially *episodic memory*) and is one of the first affected brain areas in AD dementia. The hippocampus is privileged in that neurogenesis continues within a subpart of it throughout adulthood.

Homocysteine, 129

A by-product of methionine metabolism that is dramatically elevated in children born with rare genetic abnormalities and associated with severe mental and cardiac disorders. Homocysteine can otherwise be mildly elevated due to deficits in *folate* or *B12* dietary intake, or for unknown reasons (hyperhomocysteinemia). Hyperhomocysteinemia has been connected to increased risk for cardiac disease and stroke, but more recently this has been questioned.

Hyperhomocysteinemia responds well to increased folate/B12 intake, although the clinical significance of this is contentious.

I
Inhibition, 22

A cognitive domain related to our ability to suppress our initial 'instinctual' response, reflect on a given situation, and then select the most appropriate response from a number of alternatives.

Ischemia, 53

A reduction in adequate blood supply to an organ or subpart of an organ.

L
Low-density cholesterol (LDLs) *see* **Cholesterol**, 108

M
Memory, 22

A major cognitive domain related to how we encode, retain and then retrieve information. Episodic memory refers to our memory for specific events; semantic memory refers to our stored knowledge about the world. Other memory taxonomies include visuospatial vs verbal memory, and short-term vs long-term memory, all of which may have different neurobiological underpinnings. Early AD dementia specifically affects episodic, visuospatial and short-term memory function.

Metabolic X syndrome, 87

Increasingly commonly diagnosed in middle-aged Western populations, refers to subclinical abnormalities in glucose tolerance, cholesterol, hypertension and excess weight. While an individual may fall just below the diagnostic threshold in each area, the combined weight of all these subclinical abnormalities puts them at high risk for chronic health problems.

Microvascular disease, 88

Any chronic pathology to the fine ultra-small vasculature in the brain, including capillary damage, microbleeds, micro cholesterol deposits and mini-strokes.

Mild Cognitive Impairment (MCI), 136

A state of borderline cognitive dysfunction, theoretically this syndrome sits between dementia and healthy brain ageing. MCI increases one's chances of developing dementia but not all individuals with MCI end up with dementia.

Mixed dementia, 56

A post-mortem diagnosis that is being increasingly recognised, in which individuals with clinical dementia are found to have both classical Alzheimer pathology *and* cerebrovascular pathology at autopsy. The occurrence of mixed dementia in the community is high—with rates varying between 28 and 45 per cent of all individuals with a clinical *AD dementia* diagnosis.

Myocardial infarction, 52

Death of heart muscle following cardiac ischemia, commonly referred to as a heart attack.

N

Neural stem cells (NSCs), 156

In the adult brain, refers to cells that retain a potential to replicate and then mature into one of a number of different brain cells. NSCs are therefore necessary for adult *neurogenesis*. NSCs are known to reside in two main places in the adult human: around the lining of the *ventricles* and in a subpart of the *hippocampus*.

Neurofibrillary tangles, 36

One of two pathological hallmarks of AD (along with beta-amyloid plaques). These are high-density *intracellular* aggregates of *tau*, a naturally occurring protein that makes up the neuronal cytoskeleton.

Neurogenesis, 153

A physiological process by which new neurons are
generated. During gestation, there is logically a massive level
of neurogenesis as the brain is being formed. This continues
during childhood and comes to a virtual halt by the end of
puberty. However, throughout adulthood and into late life,
neurogenesis continues to occur around the brain's ventricles,
creating cells destined for the olfactory bulb, and in the
hippocampus, which enrich local neural circuits. The
significance of human adult neurogenesis to normal memory
function and mood regulation remains hotly debated.

Neurons, 15

One of the three main classes of brain cells (along with
astrocytes and oligodendrocytes). Neurons have the critical job
of transmitting, transforming, filtering and integrating
information. Information is communicated in the form of
different firing rates. Neurons are therefore called excitable cells,
because they have a potential difference across their outer cell
membrane, which can change rapidly. A neuron is made up of a
cell body and elongated processes called dendrites and axons.
Axons communicate firing rates away from the cell body to
other neurons and are therefore myelinated by insulating fat;
dendrites receive the axonal firing patterns from other cells. The
exact point at which firing patterns are communicated from the

axon of one neurone to the dendrite of another neuron is across a microscopic gap called the synaptic junction. There are an estimated 100 million neurons in the human brain; each neuron may have up to 10,000 synaptic connections.

Neurotoxic, 35

Any process, biochemical or agent that kills neurons. Something that is neurotoxic in a petri dish (i.e. *in vitro*) may not necessarily be neurotoxic in real life (*in vivo*), and vice versa.

Neurotransmitters, 118

Neurotransmitters diffuse across the *synaptic junction* after being released as a result of an axonal impulse. They are detected on the dendritic side of the second neuron by neurotransmitter receptors. A new impluse commences when suffcent neurotransmitter receptors are activated. All drugs that affect one's mental state—from illicit drugs to alcohol, cigarettes, anesthetics and antidepressants—act in one way or another on the release and uptake of neurotransmitters at the synaptic junctions.

O

Oxidation, 73

A normal biochemical process in which an electric charge is swapped from one compound to another. Oxidation is generally balanced by the body's natural antioxidants. Excess oxidation through injury, stress or disease, however, can be harmful via the production of free radicals, which are superoxidants and can damage cells. Vitamin C is a natural antioxidant.

P

Problem solving, 22

A cognitive domain that covers our ability to adapt to a new situation, find patterns in the world, overcome a challenge, and think of alternative solutions.

Pseudodementia, 20

The occurrence of memory and other cognitive problems in older individuals with depression, to the extent that they can present as if they had dementia and make proper diagnosis difficult. Pseudodementia resolves with resolution of the underlying depression (i.e. through treatment or time); dementia just gets worse.

R

RCTs, 60

Randomised controlled trials (RCTs) are the ultimate arbiter of medical truth. Whether or not some treatment actually works (or not) for a particular condition in a particular group of patients can only be accurately assessed following a RCT. Individuals are randomly assigned to the treatment or placebo (control) condition, as if by tossing a coin, and usually remain unaware of their assignment until the end of the trial. This ensures that known and unknown background variables that may affect the result of the trial are evenly distributed between groups and hence their consequence is minimised.

Resistance exercise, 199

A type of physical exercise that involves brief bursts of activity in which major muscle groups are required to develop maximum force, practised in a repetitive fashion with breaks in between sets.

S

Somatic growth factors, 210

Molecules released into the blood circulation from the body organs (for example, muscles, liver, etc). In Chapter 8, this refers in particular to molecules released in response to physical exercise.

Stroke, 39

Aka cerebral infarction; the death of brain tissue due to loss of proper blood supply. Commonly caused by the blockage of a major cerebral blood vessel due to the build-up of fatty plaques, or the blockage of smaller blood vessels because a clot is dislodged and travels upstream. Certain cerebral blood vessels have a propensity to get blocked and therefore lead to typical symptoms when the brain region being supplied is affected. These symptoms include sudden loss of power to one side of the legs, arms or face; sudden problems in understanding, making or comprehending speech; sudden loss of vision; sudden unsteadiness on one's feet. Should any of these occur, the correct response is *call an ambulance* and get to an *Emergency Department* as quickly as possible. Time from symptom to bedside is a direct predictor of stroke outcome.

Synapses, 38

Specialised terminals at the end of axons and beginning of dendrites by which neurons communicate between each other. Neurons don't directly touch, but need to transfer information across a microscopic space between the synapses called the *synaptic junction*. An individual neuron may make thousands of synaptic connections with other neurons. AD kills off masses of synapses throughout the brain. Loss of synapses is in fact the strongest biological correlate of mental dysfunction in dementia.

Synaptic junction, 48

The microscopic space between neurons that specialises in the transfer of the information encoded in the axonal firing rate. When the electrochemical impulse reaches the synaptic junction at the end of an axon, this energy is transferred into the release of one of several dozen different types of *neurotransmitters*. When enough neurotransmitter receptors have been activated, a new impulse is formed.

Synaptogenesis, 38

The formation of new synapses between neurons, which is occurring all the time. *Enrichment* is a particularly strong stimulus for the formation of new synapses, and so complex mental activity is thought to increase synaptic numbers throughout the brain.

T

Transfer of Effect, 196

Refers to whether a clinical intervention leads to effects beyond their narrow focus. For example, physical exercise interventions demonstrate good transfer of effect because outcomes generalise not only from improvements in physical fitness but also to improvements in cognitive function. A major challenge for cognitive training (or brain training) studies is to show transfer of effect to beyond the narrow cognitive skill base that was trained.

V

Vascular Dementia, 18

A form of dementia that is caused by cerebrovascular disease, and is especially common after a stroke (up to 30 per cent of individuals within 12 months of a stroke). Early diagnosis can be difficult, because memory impairment is not as common as problems with attention, inhibition and problem solving. Coexistence of both AD dementia and Vascular Dementia in the same individual is increasingly recognised.

Ventricles, 43

Fluid-filled structures deep in the brain whose function is to produce and circulate the cerebral spinal fluid (CSF) that bathes the entire brain.

Vitamin B12, 129

An essential vitamin required for synthesis of methionine, a basic building block of proteins.

W

White matter, 43

Brain tissue composed of the axons of neurons. Since axons are covered with fatty myeline, this tissue appears paler in colour than grey matter.

Y

Younger onset dementia (YOD), 122

More than 95 per cent of all dementia cases are sporadic or late onset, meaning that they occur after about the age of 60 years. However, the needs of those with YOD (<60 years) are unique and require more attention. YOD is linked to specific mutations in genes related to the *beta-amyloid* protein in some individuals, while others have no known inheritance pattern. Also termed early-onset dementia.

References

Access Economics, *The Dementia Epidemic: Economic impact and positive solutions for Australia*, Canberra, 2003.

American Heart Association, *Fish Consumption, Fish Oil, Omega-3 Fatty Acids and Cardiovascular Disease*, November 2002.

D. Ames, and C. Ritchie, 'Antioxidants and Alzheimer's disease: Time to stop feeding vitamin E to dementia patients', *International Psychogeriatrics*, 2007, 19:1–8.

K.J. Anstey, et al., 'Smoking as a risk factor for dementia and cognitive decline: A meta-analysis of prospective studies', *American Journal of Epidemiology*, 2007, 166(4):367–78.

L. Bazzano, K. Reynolds, K. Holder and J. He, 'Effects of folic acid supplementation on risk of cardiovascular diseases:

A meta-analysis of randomised controlled trials', *JAMA*, 2006, 296:2720–6.

G. Biessels, S. Staekenborg, E Brunner, C. Brayne and P. Scheltens, 'Risk of dementia in diabetes mellitus: a systematic review', *Lancet Neurology*, 2006, 5:64–74.

A.G. Bostom, et al., 'Nonfasting plasma total homocysteine levels and stroke incidence in elderly persons: The Framingham Study', *Annals of Internal Medicine*, 1999, 131:352–5.

C. Boushey, S. Beresford, G. Omenn and A. Motulsky, 'A quantitative assessment of plasma homocysteine as a risk factor for vascular disease: Probable benefits of increasing folic acid intakes', *JAMA*, 1995, 274:1049–57.

H. Brodaty and K. Berman, 'Interventions for family caregivers of people with dementia' in R.T. Woods and L. Clare (eds), *Handbook of Clinical Psychology of Ageing*, 2nd edition, John Wiley & Sons, Chichester, UK, 2008, pp. 549–69.

H. Brodaty, A. Green and L-F. Low, 'Family carers for people with dementia' in J. O'Brien, D. Ames and A. Burns (eds), *Dementia*, 3rd edition, Arnold, London, 2005, pp. 118–31.

J.R. Cracchiolo, et al., 'Enhanced cognitive activity—over and above social or physical activity—is required to protect Alzheimer's mice against cognitive impairment, reduce A,

deposition, and increase synaptic immunoreactivity',
Neurobiology of Learning and Memory, October 2007,
88(3):277–94.

H. Dodge, et al. 'A randomized placebo-controlled trial of
ginkgo biloba for the prevention of cognitive decline',
Neurology, 2008, epublished ahead of print.

B. Draper, *Dealing with Dementia*, Allen & Unwin, Sydney, 2005.

L.R. Drew and A.S. Truswell, 'Wernicke's encephalopathy and
thiamine fortification of food: Time for a new direction?',
The Medical Journal of Australia, 1998, 168:534–5.

M. Ellinson, J. Thomas and A. Patterson, 'A critical evaluation
of the relationship between serum vitamin B12, folate
and total homocysteine with cognitive impairment in the
elderly', *Journal of Human Nutrition and Dietetic*, 2004,
17:371–83.

Y. Freund-Levi, M. Eriksdotter-Jonhagen, T. Cederholm,
H. Basun, G. Faxen-Irving, A. Garlind, I. Vedin, B. Vessby,
L.O. Wahlund and J. Palmblad, 'Omega-3 fatty acid
treatment in 174 patients with mild to moderate
Alzheimer disease: OmegAD study: a randomized double-
blind trial', *Archives of Neurology*, October 2006,
63(10):1402–8.

O. Hanon and F. Forette, 'Treatment of hypertension and
prevention of dementia', *Alzheimer's & Dementia*, 2005,
1:30–37.

G. Kempermann, *Adult Neurogenesis*, Oxford University Press, 2006.

K. Langa, N. Forster and E. Larson, 'Mixed dementia: Emerging concepts and therapeutic implications', *JAMA*, 2004, 292:2901–8.

Bruce Lee, *The Tao of Jeet Kune Do*, Ohara Publications Inc., 1975.

D.M. Lloyd-Jones, J.C. Evans and D. Levy, 'Hypertension in adults across the age spectrum: Current outcomes and control in the community', *JAMA*, 2005, 294:466–72.

M. Malouf et al, 'Folate with or without vitamin B12 for cognition and dementia', *Cochrane Review, The Cochrane Library*, Issue 4, John Wiley & Sons, Chichester, UK.

M. Mazza, A. Capuano, P. Bria and S. Mazza, 'Ginkgo biloba and donepezil: A comparison in the treatment of Alzheimer's dementia in a randomized placebo-controlled double-blind study', *European Journal of Neurology*, 2006, 13:981–5.

MRC CFAS, 'Pathological correlates of late-onset dementia in a multicentre, community-based population in England and Wales', *Lancet*, 2001, 375:169–75.

J. O'Brien et al., 'Vascular cognitive impairment', *Lancet Neurology*, 2003, 2:89–98.

G.W. Rebok et al., 'Training and maintaining memory abilities in healthy older adults: Traditional and novel approaches, *Journals of Gerontology: SERIES B*', 2007, 62B:53–61.

P. Sachdev, 'Homocysteine and brain atrophy', *Progress in Neuropsychopharmacology & Biological Psychiatry*, 2005, 29:1152–61.

P. Sachdev, Homocysteine and Alzheimer disease: an intervention study. *Nature Reviews Neurology.* 2011, 7: 9-10

M. Savaria Morris, 'Homocysteine and Alzheimer's disease', *Lancet Neurology*, 2003, 2:425–8.

S. Scheff and D.A. Price, 'Synaptic pathology in Alzheimer's disease: A review of ultrastructural studies', *Neurobiology of Aging*, 2003, 24:1029–46.

L. Shobab, G. Hsiung and H. Feldman, 'Cholesterol in Alzheimer's disease', *Lancet Neurology*, 2005, 4:841–52.

R. Terry et al., 'Physical basis of cognitive alterations in Alzheimer's disease: Synapse loss is the major correlate of cognitive impairment', *Annals of Neurology*, 1991, 30:572–80.

Understanding Younger Onset Dementia, Alzheimer's Australia Quality Dementia Care Series, 2008, available at www.alzheimers.org.au.

M. Valenzuela et al., 'Neural stem cells for neuropsychiatric disorders', *Acta Neuropsychiatrica*, 2007, 19:11–26.

M. Valenzuela et al. 'Lifespan mental activity predicts diminished rate of hippocampal atrophy', *PLoS One*, 2008, 3(7):e2598.

M. Valenzuela, M. Breakspear and P. Sachdev, 'Complex mental activity: Molecular, cellular and cortical network mechanisms', *Brain Research Reviews*, 2007, in press.

M. Valenzuela and P. Sachdev, 'Can cognitive exercise prevent the onset of dementia? A systematic review of randomized clinical trials with longitudinal follow up', *American Journal of Geriatric Psychiatry*, 2008, in press.

J. Verghese et al., 'Leisure activities and the risk of dementia in the elderly', *New England Journal of Medicine*, 2003, 348:2508–16.

S.L. Willis et al., 'Long-term effects of cognitive training on everyday functional outcomes in older adults', *JAMA*, 2006, 296:2805–14.

B. Wolozin, 'Cholesterol and the biology of Alzheimer's disease', *Neuron*, 2004, 41:7–10.

Index